Best Practices in Reading

NEW EDITION

Level C

in Reading

Best Practices in Reading, Level C, New Edition
OT127
ISBN-13: 978-0-7836-9332-3

Triumph Learning® 136 Madison Avenue, 7th Floor, New York, NY 10016

Printed in the United States of America.

15 14 13 12 11 10 9 8 7 6 5 4 3   HPS250461

TABLE OF CONTENTS

Alex wants to stay cool on this hot, sticky day. But are those black clouds in the distance bringing danger?

Think About Genre

One type of literature is **fiction**. Fiction stories are made up by authors, but they may tell about events that could really happen. That is true for this **adventure** story, "Dangerous Storm."

What do you think happens in an adventure story? Fill in the bubble beside the two sentences that tell about an adventure story.

Ⓐ It may be exciting.

Ⓑ It tells about something that really happened.

Ⓒ It tells how to make something.

Ⓓ The characters may face danger.

Think About the Topic

Read the introduction to "Dangerous Storm" again. Ask yourself: *What kinds of storms are dangerous?* Write two kinds of storms below.

1. _____

2. _____

Preview and Predict

Look at the story. Read the title and look at the pictures. Write what you think "Dangerous Storm" will be about?

_____

_____

_____

STRATEGIES

QUESTION
MAKE INFERENCES
UNDERSTAND GENRE
VISUALIZE

DANGEROUS STORM

QUESTION
Ask yourself questions to better understand a story.

Where are Alex and Grandpa? They are in a boat fishing on the lake.

Why did Grandpa say "got out of the lake just in time"?

"I don't like the look of that sky," said Grandpa. "Let's go home."

"Can't we stay here at the lake and let the rain cool us off?" asked Alex.

The weather was hot and sticky. Fishing in Grandpa's boat was the best thing to happen all day.

"I think we're in for quite a storm," Grandpa said.

By the time they reached shore, a breeze was stirring the air. Suddenly, a flash of lightning ran across the sky. Then they heard loud thunder.

"I'd say we got out of the lake just in time!" said Grandpa.

"Yeah," Alex agreed. He knew it was dangerous to be in the water during a thunderstorm.

The sky looked black. Grandpa's old truck bumped along the gravel road. Before he and Alex reached the highway, hailstones were beating down everywhere.

hailstones (HALE-stohnz) small round pieces of ice that fall like rain

"It's not safe to be on the road," said Grandpa. "Let's head for Aunt Lou's farm."

Aunt Lou lived on a farm just outside of town. As they pulled into her driveway, Alex saw a strange, dark, V-shaped cloud.

"Tornado!" shouted Grandpa as he jumped from the truck. "Head for the cellar. I'll help Aunt Lou!"

Aunt Lou called from her porch. "Where's Lady?"

"I'll get her," said Alex. "I saw her go into the shed."

Lady was Aunt Lou's German shepherd. Alex ran toward the shed. Two voices called him back, but he didn't hear them.

Just then the shed door flew off and sailed up. The wind roared like a jet plane. There was no time to run back into the cellar. The tornado was here!

MAKE INFERENCES

Sometimes the author doesn't tell you everything. Use what the author does tell you and what you already know to figure out something.

Why does Grandpa say, "Head for the cellar"? I think that must be a safe place during a tornado.

Why did the adults call Alex back?

cellar (SEL-ur) a room that is below ground

tornado (tor-NAY-do) a violent windstorm

UNDERSTAND GENRE

(adventure story)
When Alex is in the cellar, the author tells you about the dangerous storm. This helps make an adventure story exciting. Two words that the author uses to make the storm sound dangerous are

_____

and _____ .

VISUALIZE

Sometimes you have to make a picture of the story in your mind to understand the story better. What does Aunt Lou's yard look like in the story? Draw what you "see" below.

Alex thought fast. He remembered an old root cellar next to the shed. It was like a small cave.

"Here, Lady," he called. "Come with me!" He pulled the big dog out of the shed and into the cellar. Lady was shaking.

The storm crashed and roared over their heads. Alex gently stroked Lady's fur.

Then the wind became quiet. Alex looked out. He stared, surprised. The shed was gone! Aunt Lou and Grandpa were coming toward him.

They could not believe what the tornado left behind. Aunt Lou's porch was in ruins. Power lines were down. Broken boards, tree branches, and smashed flowerpots lay everywhere in her yard.

"You've got a lot of damage here, Lou," said Grandpa.

Aunt Lou just smiled. "We're all safe," she said. "That's what really matters!"

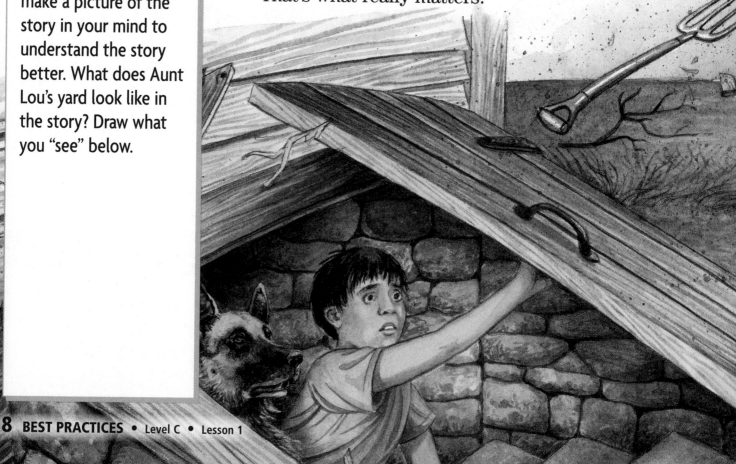

Identify Cause and Effect

A cause is the reason why something happens. An effect is what happens.

Read each cause in the chart below. Then write the effect, or what happened, in the box next to it.

Why It Happened (Cause)	What Happened (Effect)
A storm is coming.	Grandpa and Alex leave the lake.
The weather is too dangerous for driving.	
Aunt Lou can't find her dog.	
Alex cannot get back to Grandpa and Aunt Lou.	

Summarize

You can tell a friend what a story is about by giving a summary.

   Write a short summary of "Dangerous Storm." Tell how the characters solved some big problems.

_____

_____

_____

_____

_____

_____

> A summary is short, so I will tell only the most important things in the story. I will tell them in order, from beginning to end.

Identify Details

When you summarize a story, you tell only the most important ideas. Leave out less important details in the story.

   Read each sentence below. Fill in the bubble beside the two best sentences to include in a summary of this story.

Ⓐ Grandpa's pickup truck is old.

Ⓑ Grandpa and Alex see a tornado coming.

Ⓒ Lady is a German shepherd.

Ⓓ Alex runs to the shed to get Lady.

Ⓔ Power lines are down in Aunt Lou's yard.

Tornadoes

Some people say that tornadoes are the worst weather on Earth. In this article, you will learn about these violent storms and why they are so dangerous.

Think About Genre

The story "Dangerous Storm" is fiction. Another type of literature is **nonfiction**. Nonfiction tells about real people, places, and things. "Tornadoes" is a **nonfiction article** that gives facts.

In nonfiction articles, authors help readers understand new information. For example, short sections with headings help readers see important parts of what the article is about. Quickly look over this nonfiction article. What do you see that helps a reader? Put an **X** next to each thing that you see.

_____ photographs

_____ headings that shows sections

_____ animal characters that walk like people

_____ maps that help you understand information

Think About the Topic

Read the introduction to "Tornadoes" again. Ask yourself: *What did I learn about tornadoes from reading the adventure story, "Dangerous Storm"?* Write one thing you learned on the lines below.

_____

_____

_____

Preview and Predict

Now that you have read the title and looked at the article, think about what you saw. Write one question that you think this article will answer.

_____

_____

_____

STRATEGIES

VISUALIZE
QUESTION
UNDERSTAND GENRE

Tornadoes

VISUALIZE
Make a "picture" in your mind of what an author describes.

The author compares a tornado to a funnel. I've seen a funnel, so now I know the shape of a tornado.

A tornado is also compared to a vacuum cleaner. What do you imagine?

_____

_____

_____

column (KAL-um)
something long and upright
funnel (FUN-ul) a tube
that is wide at the top and
narrow at the bottom

Think about a storm so strong that it can:

• pick up a school bus and carry it through the air.
• pull large trees up out of the ground and throw them around like toys.
• move a house to a different place.

Tornadoes really are that strong!

What Is a Tornado?

A tornado is a very strong windstorm. Tornadoes are often called "twisters." This is because a tornado is a twisting column of air. The air is shaped like a funnel. When it touches the ground, it acts like a vacuum cleaner. It sucks dirt and objects up into the air.

Why Are Tornadoes So Dangerous?

The wind around the funnel of a tornado reaches speeds of up to 300 miles per hour. Tornadoes have the fastest winds of any storm on Earth. They destroy almost everything in their path.

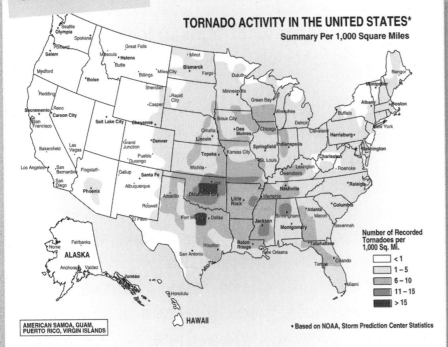

TORNADO ACTIVITY IN THE UNITED STATES*
Summary Per 1,000 Square Miles

Number of Recorded Tornadoes per 1,000 Sq. Mi.

< 1
1 – 5
6 – 10
11 – 15
> 15

* Based on NOAA, Storm Prediction Center Statistics

AMERICAN SAMOA, GUAM, PUERTO RICO, VIRGIN ISLANDS

When and Where Do Tornadoes Happen?

Tornadoes usually begin inside thunderstorms. They can happen in any season of the year. Most tornadoes occur during the spring and summer. They can also happen in any state in the United States. They most often occur in the midwestern and eastern states. One part of the Midwest has so many tornadoes, it is known as "Tornado Alley."

Is a Hurricane the Same as a Tornado?

Tornadoes and hurricanes are both whirlwinds. One difference between the two storms is that hurricanes are much larger than tornadoes. A hurricane may be hundreds of miles wide!

Here are some other ways they are different. Hurricanes begin over oceans. They grow slowly and last for many days. Tornadoes do not last long, but they have much faster winds.

QUESTION
As you read, ask yourself questions to see if you can figure things out.

Why did the author write about both hurricanes and tornadoes? Maybe some people mix up these two kinds of storms.

Do many tornadoes happen in your state? Use the map to explain your answer.

_____

_____

_____

_____

whirlwinds (WURL-winds) air that is spinning and twisting very fast

What Can You Do to Stay Safe in a Tornado?

Before a tornado comes, you should do two things. First, learn what signs to look for in the weather. Second, plan where you will go for shelter.

If you see that a bad storm is on the way, listen to a radio or watch TV to find out more. Don't panic. Go to a safe place as quickly as possible.

What places are safe during a tornado? A storm cellar or basement is best. If there is no basement, go to the lowest level of the building. If you are at school, go to an inside hallway.

What places are unsafe during a tornado? Stay out of a big open space, such as a gym. Stay away from windows where there may be flying glass. Stay away from power lines. A car is not a safe place either.

A tornado is scary, but you can stay safe if you know what to do.

TORNADO DANGER SIGNS

- Sky turns greenish black
- Air is very still
- Dark funnel-shaped cloud appears
  These are just three possible signs of a tornado coming.

If there is a tornado while you are at school, follow your teacher's directions.

Compare and Contrast

Reread the section with the heading that asks, "Is a Hurricane the Same as a Tornado?" Then complete the Venn diagram by filling in each part with one of the following words or phrases. The first two have been done for you.

- hundreds of miles across
- develops over the ocean
- doesn't last long
- whirlwind

- fastest winds of any storm
- lasts for many days
- can be dangerous

Trees can be torn out of the ground by a tornado.

Tornado   **Hurricane**

fastest winds of any storm   **Both**   hundreds of miles across

_____   _____   _____

_____   _____   _____

_____   _____   _____

_____   _____   _____

_____   _____   _____

Summarize

Summarize the section that tells how hurricanes and tornadoes are the same and how they are different. Use the diagram on page 15 to help you write your summary below.

_____

_____

_____

_____

_____

> First I will write the heading "Is a Hurricane the Same as a Tornado?" Next, I will tell how hurricanes and tornadoes are the same. Then I will tell how each is different.

Identify the Main Ideas

Each section of this article begins with a question. Then it is followed by information that answers the question. This helps you understand the main idea, or most important idea, in that part of the article. Read each heading below. Then reread those sections of the article. Write the main idea of each section. The first one has been done for you.

1. "What Is a Tornado?"

Main Idea: __A tornado is a strong windstorm._____

2. "Why Are Tornadoes So Dangerous?"

Main Idea: _____

3. "What Can You Do to Stay Safe in a Tornado?"

Main Idea: _____

Make Connections

Think about how the two selections connect to each other and to you. Answer the following questions.

1. What did the characters in "Dangerous Storm" do to be safe in the storm?

_____

_____

_____

2. What kind of storm has happened where you live? Write about it.

_____

_____

_____

3. What are two examples of what can happen in a tornado?

A. _____

_____

B. _____

_____

Weather forecasters help predict exact locations of storms.

Write a Plan of Action

Write two things you need to do to stay safe if you hear a tornado warning. Next to number 3, write what you should NOT do.

1. _____

_____

2. _____

_____

3. _____

_____

Hurricanes viewed from space.

 Before you write, use the *Emergency!* handout your teacher will give you to plan your plan of action.

Plan Your Research

Write two questions you still have about tornadoes or other bad storms. Use books or the Internet to find and write answers to your questions.

1. _____

_____

2. _____

_____

The Field of Freaky Flowers

It can't be easy being an insect. Just about every creature on Earth is bigger. Some plants can even mean danger—as you'll discover in this "freaky" fantasy story.

Think About Genre

Fiction stories are made up. Some can seem real, and some can never happen. **Fantasy** is one kind of fiction. Impossible things can happen in a fantasy. Animals might talk, or plants might dance. Anything you can imagine can happen in a fantasy.

Fill in the circles next to two things that could happen only in a fantasy.

Ⓐ Spiders play guitars.

Ⓑ A dog gets lost.

Ⓒ A boy is two inches tall.

Ⓓ Thunder booms.

Think About the Topic

Read the introduction to "The Field of Freaky Flowers" again. Ask yourself: *Why might some plants be dangerous for an insect?* Write one idea.

_____

_____

_____

_____

Preview and Predict

Look through the story. Then look at the title and illustrations. What do you think you will read about in "The Field of Freaky Flowers"?

_____

_____

_____

_____

The Field of Freaky Flowers

STRATEGIES

**VISUALIZE
MAKE INFERENCES
UNDERSTAND GENRE
MAKE CONNECTIONS**

VISUALIZE

The author gives details about how the fantasy characters look and what they do. The details help you picture them.

> Ma Dragonfly shakes her antennae at her kids the way a human mom shakes her finger.

How do you imagine Red and Lucky?

Red and Lucky sat on a log at the edge of the swamp. Ma Dragonfly fluttered over the log. They'd all been arguing. "I know you boys want to go fishing by yourselves," Ma Dragonfly said. "I just don't know if you two are ready to go alone."

"WE'RE READY!" they shouted together.

"Then prove it," she said, shaking her antennae at them. "Tell me my three rules."

Red and Lucky wiggled their wings impatiently. Then they recited the rules. "*One:* Fly straight. *Two:* Don't talk to the ducks. *Three:* Stay away from the Field of Freaky Flowers."

"Okay, boys! You can go," Ma said.

But Ma Dragonfly still worried. As her boys flew off, she shouted after them. "DON'T FORGET! STAY AWAY FROM THE FIELD OF FREAKY FLOWERS. IT'S DANGEROUS!"

---

antennae (an-TEN-uh) long feelers on the head of an insect

recited (rih-SITE-id) said aloud from memory

Soon Red and Lucky saw the pond sparkling below. They zipped over its clear surface, catching one water flea after another. They found mosquito eggs, too.

"YUM! YUM! YUM!" they both said, many times.

Lucky and Red fished and ate, fished and ate, fished and ate. Soon their bags were full. They knew they should head home to Ma Dragonfly.

"Have you ever seen the Field of Freaky Flowers?" Red asked Lucky.

"No, have you?" Lucky replied.

"Of course not. But I wonder what it looks like."

"Are you thinking the same thing I'm thinking?"

Soon the two dragonflies were flying as fast as their wings could carry them—straight to the Field of Freaky Flowers.

"Those yellow flowers look like pitchers," said Red.

"Those green plants look like clams," added Lucky. They both laughed.

"They don't look dangerous at all!"

"Not one bit."

MAKE INFERENCES
Sometimes story characters surprise us. Look for clues in the story. Try to figure out why characters act the way they do.

I know why Red and Lucky didn't go right home. They were having too much fun.

Why didn't Red and Lucky follow Ma Dragonfly's rules about the Field of Freaky Flowers?

pitcher (PICH-er) a container with a spout

A moment later, Lucky flew over a yellow plant shaped like a jug. "I bet there are some delicious fleas in there. I'll take a peek." Lucky landed on it.

"What do you see, Lucky?" Red asked.

"Nothing yet," he answered, and then—he fell in! "HELP!" he shouted.

"What's wrong?" Red yelled.

"It's sticky in here. AHHHH!"

Red flew over the yellow plant. "I'm coming in," he said.

"Don't!" shouted Lucky. "You'll just get stuck."

Just then, Red spotted a long piece of thick grass. He pulled it out of the ground, flew over to the plant, and slipped it inside.

"What's that?" called Lucky from down below.

"It's a grass rope. Grab on," Red said. "I'll pull you out." And that's just what Red did.

Then the two dragonflies were happily on their way home, and they never ever visited the Field of Freaky Flowers again!

delicious (dih-LISH-us)
yummy, tasty

Identify Parts of a Story

All stories have characters, a setting where the story takes place, and events that happen. Most stories have a problem that gets solved at the end. Review the story to help you fill in the rest of the chart.

Characters

_____

_____

_____

Settings

swamp, pond, Field of Freaky Flowers

Problem

Red and Lucky disobey. They go where they shouldn't go, and Lucky gets stuck.

Important Events

1. _____
2. _____
3. _____

Solution

_____

Summarize

A good summary is a short retelling of the story that includes the most important events and leaves out details that are not as important.

Imagine that you are Red or Lucky. Tell your friends about your adventure. Use the chart on page 23 to help you.

_____

_____

_____

_____

_____

Identify Details

Figuring out what's important helps to make a good summary. If you leave out a detail, and it does not change the story, then the detail is probably not very important and should not be in the summary.

Decide which sentences below tell important parts of the story. Put an **X** in front of two sentences that are not very important.

_____ Red and Lucky are young dragonflies.

_____ Ma Dragonfly decides to let Red and Lucky go fishing.

_____ Red and Lucky love eating water fleas.

_____ The mosquito eggs taste great.

_____ Red and Lucky decide to go to the Field of Freaky Flowers.

Dragonflies don't really talk about freaky flowers. But some plants *are* dangerous for insects and spiders. In this science article, you can read about these plants. It's stranger than fiction!

Think About Genre

In a fantasy story, an author uses imagination. A fantasy may have strange, made-up creatures and events. In **nonfiction**, the information is true. Nonfiction authors give facts to help you think about information. Some of the facts, like those in this **science article**, can be very strange!

Preview "Plants with Traps." Put an **X** beside three things you find in the article.

_____ photographs

_____ headings

_____ bugs that talk

_____ facts about plants

Venus Flytraps

Think About the Topic

Read the introduction to "Plants with Traps" again. What did you read in "The Field of Freaky Flowers" that might be true? Complete the following sentence.

Plants can be _____

_____ .

Preview and Predict

Preview the article again. Predict two things you think you might learn about plants with traps.

1. _____

_____

2. _____

_____

Plants with Traps

QUESTION

When reading new information, ask yourself questions to test your understanding.

Write a question you have about the information on this page. Then reread to find the answer. Draw a line under the answer.

_____

_____

_____

_____

_____

dewdrops (DOO-drops) little drops of water

species (SPEE-sheez) kinds or types of plants or animals

Insects, Beware!

A fly buzzes over a tiny green plant called the sundew. The sundew plant sparkles. It seems to be covered with **dewdrops**. It smells sweet. The fly lands on the plant. Now it's in trouble!

The fly's feet stick to the plant. The fly tries to escape, but the little hairs of the plant bend and trap it. The fly becomes food for the sundew plant.

Sundew plants are usually less than one inch tall.

Types of Insect-Eating Plants

The sundew is an insect-eating plant. Sometimes insect-eating plants are called carnivorous (car-NIV-er-us). This word means "meat eating." There are about 450 different **species** of insect-eating plants. They are found on all the continents—except for the frozen region of Antarctica.

These plants have different colors, shapes, sizes, and smells. They come in green, yellow, red, and even purple. They range in size from less than one inch to about two feet tall.

All insect-eating plants grow only in wet areas. These are floating bladderworts.

UNDERSTAND GENRE

(science article)
Turning the headings of a science article into questions can help you understand what you will read about.

I can turn the first heading on page 26 into a question: Why should insects beware? Some plants can kill insects.

Look at the heading on this page. First, write it as a question. Then write the answer.

Question:

_____

_____

Answer:

_____

_____

Plants with Traps

These kinds of plants can't chase their prey. Because they don't have legs or wings, their prey must come to them. Like other plants, insect-eating plants have colors and smells that attract insects. Some of these plants also eat small animals, like frogs or even mice. One example of an animal-eating plant is the bladderwort, which dines on tiny water animals.

To catch their food, animal-eating and insect-eating plants have traps. Some are moving traps and some are still traps.

- **Moving traps** have parts that clamp, swing open, or close. Sundew plants have moving traps, like bladderworts and Venus flytraps.
- **Still traps** don't move. Instead, the plants ooze sticky glue or slippery goop. Pitcher plants have still traps.

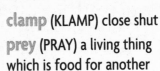

clamp (KLAMP) close shut
prey (PRAY) a living thing which is food for another living thing

© Options Publishing. No copying permitted.

A Moving Trap

The Venus flytrap is the most well-known of all insect-eating plants. White flowers grow on it in the spring. But the plant's leaves are its traps. Each leaf is shaped like a clamshell. Along the curved edge are stiff bristles. Touching the bristles inside the trap causes the two sides of the leaf to snap shut. Juices flow from the leaf. These juices break down the insect's body for the plant to use as food.

A Still Trap

The pitcher plant is shaped like a thin jug. The inside walls of this plant have slippery hairs or waxy goop. Insects lose their footing and slip down . . . down . . . down. Some pitcher plants have water in the bottom. The insects drown. Other pitcher plants make juices to kill their prey.

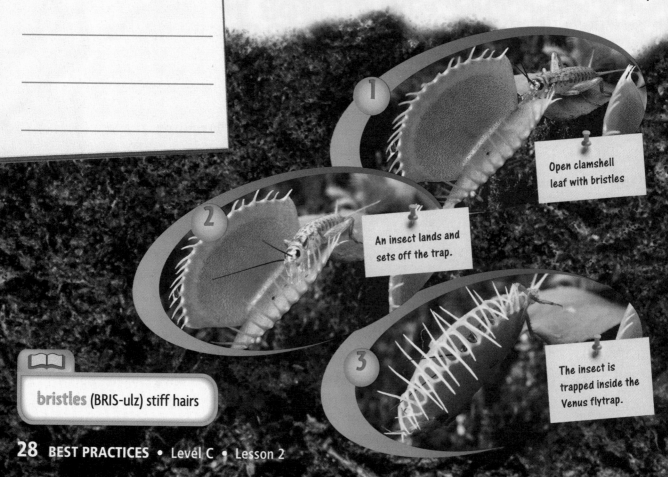

1 Open clamshell leaf with bristles

2 An insect lands and sets off the trap.

3 The insect is trapped inside the Venus flytrap.

bristles (BRIS-ulz) stiff hairs

Identify Details

Use the word web below to write details about the two kinds of plants on page 28. Some words have been filled in for you.

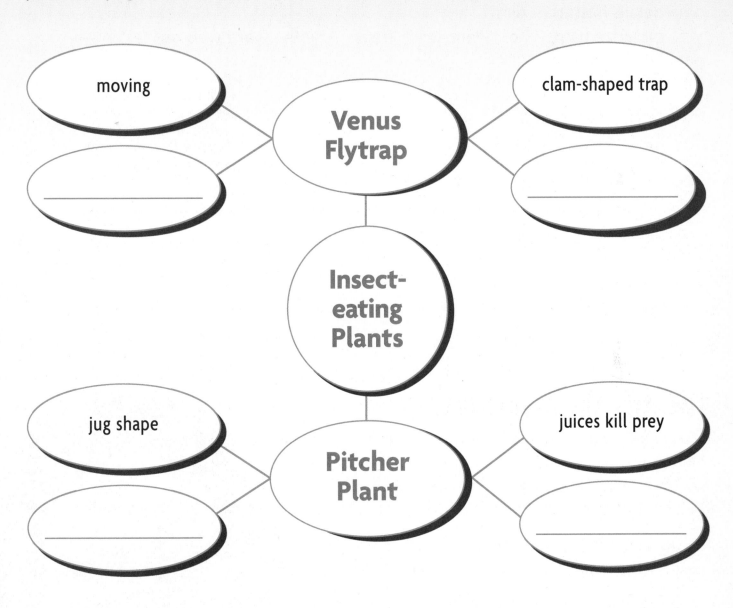

moving

Venus Flytrap

clam-shaped trap

_____

_____

Insect-eating Plants

jug shape

Pitcher Plant

juices kill prey

_____

_____

Summarize

A summary is a brief retelling of what you read. It can cover a whole article or just one part of it. If you summarize only one part, you include only details from that part.

Summarize page 28 of "Plants with Traps." Use the word web on page 29 to help you.

> I will start my summary with the name of the section and explain what it is about. Then I'll describe the two examples of insect-eating plants.

_____

_____

_____

_____

_____

Identify the Main Ideas

Main ideas are the most important ideas in an article. Details are pieces of information that tell more about the main idea. Read each sentence below. Then fill in the bubble next to the main idea.

1. Ⓐ Animal-eating and insect-eating plants have traps.

   Ⓑ These plants have parts that swing, clamp, or snap.

2. Ⓐ The sundew is one kind of insect-eating plant.

   Ⓑ There are about 450 kinds of insect-eating plants.

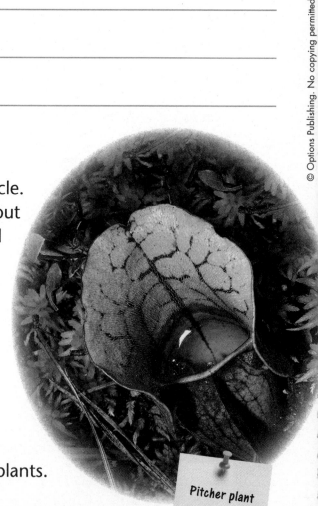

Pitcher plant

Make Connections

Think about how the two selections you just read connect to each other. Answer the following questions.

1. Both the fantasy story and the science article are about insect-eating plants. What information about insect-eating plants is the same?

_____

_____

2. Think about what you learned in the article. What could have happened to Lucky if Red wasn't there to help him?

_____

_____

3. Which insect-eating or animal-eating plant trap is the most interesting to you? Why?

_____

_____

4. If Ma Dragonfly read the article, what could she have told them about the plants in the field?

_____

_____

Write an Opinion

Do you think it would be good to have a garden with insect-eating plants? Write your opinion (what you think) in a complete sentence. Then support your opinion by explaining why you think this way.

Opinion: _____

Reason: _____

_____

 Before you write, use the *Meat-Eating Plants!* handout your teacher will give you to write your opinion.

Plan Your Research

Choose one plant you want to learn more about. Write two questions you would like to find answers to. Use books or the Internet to find answers.

Floating bladderworts

1. _____

_____

_____

2. _____

_____

_____

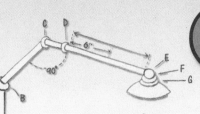

Julia's Solution

Julia loves reading stories and wants to be a writer. But she wishes she had more time to read or write her own stories. She's good at science and inventing things. Can she invent something to solve her problem?

Think About Genre

In **realistic fiction**, the events described could really happen. Settings seem real, too. The characters are like people you might know. Authors make up what happens in realistic fiction, but these stories seem like they could happen in real life.

Write three things that a character in a realistic fiction story might do.

_____

_____

_____

Think About the Topic

You can tell from the introduction that the story you are going to read is about inventions. Think about what you know about inventions. Write about an invention that you use everyday.

_____

_____

_____

Preview and Predict

Take a quick look at the story. Read the title and look at the pictures. Predict one idea about Julia's invention.

_____

_____

_____

STRATEGIES

MAKE PREDICTIONS
DRAW CONCLUSIONS
QUESTION
UNDERSTAND GENRE

Julia's Solution

MAKE PREDICTIONS
Use details in a story to help you predict what might happen next.

I can see that Julia has many books. She likes to read.

How do you think Julia might try to become a faster reader?

"Julia," Ms. Rivera called, "Lights out, my little bookworm!"

Julia groaned. Once again, she had not finished the story. She closed the book and said goodnight to the exciting tale of the traveling space ship.

Her uncle knew Julia wanted to be a writer. He had given her some fiction books, and she loved them. But after soccer and homework, Julia never had enough time to finish the stories. Bedtime seemed to come too soon. She loved learning new words, but looking them up took time, too. If only she could read faster! She wanted to start writing her own stories, but there was no time.

Julia and her older sister Cristina loved science and inventing gadgets. They had lots of tools and diagrams.

Julia fell asleep wondering whether they could make something that would help her read faster.

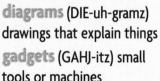

diagrams (DIE-uh-gramz) drawings that explain things
gadgets (GAHJ-itz) small tools or machines

DRAW CONCLUSIONS
Use what you read to figure out other information about a character or event.

Why did Julia call her invention the Speedy Reader?

Over the next few days, Julia thought about fun ideas that could help her when she reads. When her class went to the library, she spent her time digging through books about inventions. Finally, an idea came to her as she left school on Friday. She raced home to share her idea with Cristina.

The sisters spent Saturday afternoon building gadgets. They used different tools and a battery. They tested a few gadgets to see if they would work. Then the sisters started working on two final inventions. Julia smiled as they worked. She thought about herself reading faster and learning new words to use in her writing.

At last, they finished! They called the first invention a Speedy Reader. Julia pressed a pedal with her foot every time she finished a page. A suction cup grabbed the page and turned it for her! It was so much fun. Julia read three stories in little time.

The second invention helped with studying new words. Julia called this the Flashcard Flipper. Julia read the word on one side of a card and guessed the **definition**. Then she pressed a green button.

QUESTION
Ask yourself questions about ideas that are not clear.

Explain how Speedy Reader works. Reread and look at the picture.

definitions (def-uh-NISH-unz) the meanings of words

© Options Publishing. No copying permitted.

The Flashcard Flipper automatically flipped the card so Julia could check her answer. If her answer was right, she pressed a blue button. Then the card would fall into a basket of correct answers. If the answer was wrong, the Flashcard Flipper dropped the card into another basket. Julia then pressed the green button to study those words again.

Julia learned tons of new words! She was proud. Cristina called her a great problem solver.

Julia now had more time to read and to write her own stories because of her inventions. Her first story was called "Adventures of the Sisters Who Invent." She planned to enter this story in a writing contest.

The next day at school, Julia's teacher asked the class to write about what they want to be when they grow up. Julia had no problem with this task. She wanted to be the same thing she was now: a writer!

automatically (aw-tuh-MAHT-ih-cuh-lee) working on its own

Understand Character

You learned about the main character, Julia, by what she did in the story.

Read the sentence in each box. It describes Julia. Then write one example from the story that explains why she can be described this way.

Julia is a problem solver.

Example: _____

_____

Julia loves reading.

Example: _____

_____

Julia works well with others.

Example: _____

_____

Julia's Solution

Summarize

Write a short summary of "Julia's Solution." Write one sentence that tells about the beginning of the story, one or two that tell about the middle, and one sentence that tells the ending. Include only the most important events.

_____

_____

_____

_____

_____

_____

_____

Identify Sequence

Think about the order of events in the story. Read the events below from "Julia's Solution." Number the events in the order that they happened.

_____ Julia writes about being a writer when she grows up.

_____ Julia uses her Speedy Reader as she reads.

_____ Julia thinks about a way to read faster.

_____ Julia uses the Flashcard Flipper.

_____ Julia and her sister make the inventions.

LESSON
3
NONFICTION

Paths to
Inventing

Have you ever thought about inventing something? People invent things for different reasons. Inventions happen in different ways. Read ahead to learn more about some inventions that you have likely seen or used.

Think About Genre

Photographs in a **nonfiction article** often give you important information. Captions are the words that help you understand the photographs. Look at the photographs in this article and read the captions. What do they show you about the topic?

_____

_____

_____

Think About the Topic

Reread the introduction to "Paths to Inventing." Think about something you use a lot at school or at home. What is a new way you can use that item? Write your idea below.

_____

_____

Preview and Predict

Look through the article again. This time, read the headings. Predict one thing you will learn about inventions as you read the article.

_____

_____

_____

Windshield wipers make cars safer to drive in the rain.

STRATEGIES

MAKE PREDICTIONS
MAKE INFERENCES
MAKE CONNECTIONS

Paths to Inventing

People have always been inventing things. But not everything is invented in the same way. Some inventions make others better. Some happen when people are trying to solve a problem. Other inventions happened by accident.

Windshield Wipers

When it rained in the early 1900s, people in cars had to stop on the side of the road. They would get out of their car and wipe the windshield clean. During a bad storm, they stopped often.

On a long drive from Alabama to New York in 1903, Mary Anderson wondered if there was a better and faster way to clean the windshield. She invented a rubber blade device. It swung across the windshield to remove water. After about ten years, Anderson's invention could be found on most cars.

MAKE PREDICTIONS
As you read, think about what the article might teach you next.

> I read that it took ten years for windshield wipers to be found on cars.

Why do you think it took a long time for cars to have the invention?

_____

_____

_____

_____

device (dih-VISE) something made for a special purpose

windshield (WIND-sheeld) glass that covers the front of a car

All cars use Anderson's invention when driving in the rain.

At first, some people thought Anderson's invention was silly. Others were afraid that the wipers would keep them from seeing the road. As time passed, people learned that windshield wipers made driving cars safer and more **efficient**. Today, it's hard to imagine cars without windshield wipers!

The Sticky Note

Spencer Silver was a scientist. He set out to invent a strong glue, but he ended up inventing a **weak** glue. It stuck to objects, but it was also easy to peel off. Over the years, he told many people about his weak glue.

Art Fry was one of these people. In 1974, he came up with the idea that Silver's glue should be on bookmarks. That way, they would not slip out of books. Today, people around the world have found many uses for sticky notes.

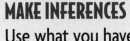
MAKE INFERENCES
Use what you have read and what you know to figure out new things about a topic.

I'm glad sticky notes were invented. I use them a lot.

What might have happened if Spencer had never told anyone about his weak glue?

_____

_____

_____

_____

Today, many kinds of sticky-note products are sold.

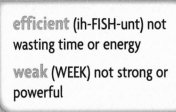
efficient (ih-FISH-unt) not wasting time or energy

weak (WEEK) not strong or powerful

MAKE CONNECTIONS
Connect what you have read to your own life.

Frank Epperson's drink froze because he left it out in very cold weather.

What happens when you put water in a freezer?

_____

Why does this happen?

_____

_____

_____

_____

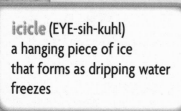

icicle (EYE-sih-kuhl)
a hanging piece of ice that forms as dripping water freezes

Frank Epperson with his granddaughter

The Ice Pop

In 1905, an eleven-year-old boy invented the ice pop on his porch by accident. One chilly, fall day, Frank Epperson mixed a fruity drink using powder and water. But he forgot the drink outside, with a stirring stick in the cup. It got very cold during the night. This made the drink freeze. In the morning, Frank used the stirring stick to pull out the frozen treat. He showed it to his friends and called it the "Epperson icicle." Frank didn't mean to, but he had invented the ice pop!

Almost twenty years later, Epperson remembered his invention while working at an amusement park lemonade stand. He thought that people would love to buy his frozen treats. Epperson made seven fruit flavors. Ice pops are still popular today.

Compare and Contrast

The article you just read describes how some inventions happened. Some things about these inventions are the same. Some are different.

Use the Venn diagram to compare and contrast two inventions. On the left, write two ideas that are true for only the wiper blades. On the right, write two ideas that are true for only the sticky note. In the center, write two ways they are the same.

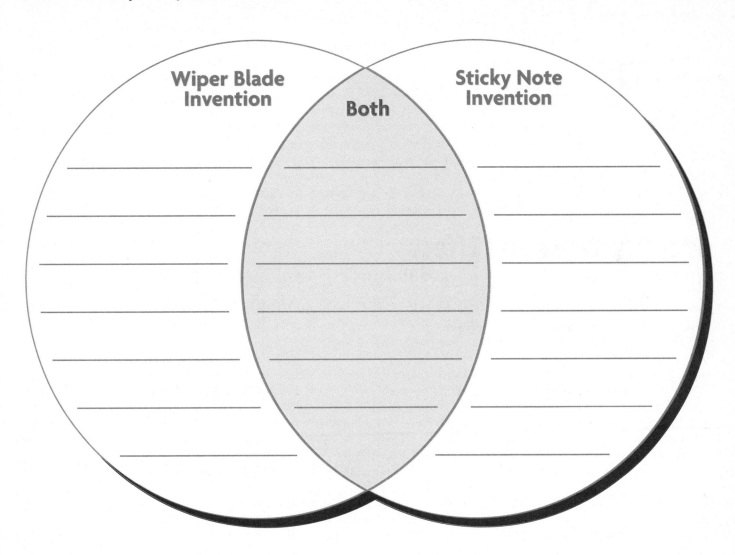

Summarize

A brief summary tells what an article is mostly about. It should include only the most important ideas about each section of the article.

Complete each sentence below. The finished sentences will be a short summary of "Paths to Inventing."

"Paths to Inventing" is mostly about _____.

The first invention is _____. It _____

_____.

The second invention is _____. It _____

_____.

The third invention is _____. It _____

_____.

Identify Cause and Effect

The sticky note and ice pop were both invented by accident. Read the parts of the chart that are filled in. Use what you learned about the inventions to complete the chart.

Cause (Why It Happened)	Effect (What Happened)
_____ _____	Art Fry used the weak glue to invent the sticky note.
Frank Epperson left his drink outside.	_____ _____

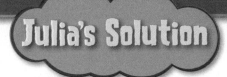

Make Connections

Think about "Julia's Solution" and "Paths to Inventing." Answer the following questions that connect the two selections to each other and to you.

1. What are two ways Julia's invention and the sticky note could help students?

_____

_____

_____

2. What are two ways Julia and Frank Epperson are different?

_____

_____

_____

3. Think about something you use a lot or really enjoy. Why is it important to you? What would you do if it had not been invented?

_____

_____

_____

Write Directions

Think about something that you use every day at school. Pretend that you have just invented it. No one else knows how to use it yet. On the lines below, write step-by-step directions for using the invention. Then draw a diagram of it on another paper to help people understand.

_____

_____

_____

_____

_____

Before you write, use the *My Invention* handout your teacher will give you to plan and draw your invention.

Plan Your Research

Think about another invention that you use at home. Write three questions you have about it. Then use books or the Internet to find your answers.

1. _____

2. _____

3. _____

```
┌─────────────────────────────────┐
│         GETTING READY            │
└─────────────────────────────────┘
```

LESSON
4
FICTION

Journey of Wonder

Do you know there are places in the world that were not built by people?
Nature put them there. Amazing! They are called "natural wonders."
Imagine taking a trip to a natural wonder 200 years ago!

Think About Genre

All stories of **fiction** are made up. Some of them use real facts from long ago to tell a story. These stories are called **historical fiction**. Both people who once lived and made-up characters are in a story about real events in history.

Fill in the bubble that best tells what you find in historical fiction.

(A) All events are true.

(B) Real and made-up characters tell a story about real events in history.

(C) All events are make-believe.

Think About the Topic

Read the introduction to "Journey of Wonder" again. It gives you an idea of what a natural wonder is. Something that is built by people is not a natural wonder. Write the name of an amazing place that you think could be a natural wonder.

_____

_____

_____

Preview and Predict

Take a quick look at the story. Read the title and look at the pictures. Write one thing you think you will read about in the story "Journey of Wonder."

_____

_____

STRATEGIES

DRAW CONCLUSIONS
QUESTION
UNDERSTAND GENRE
VISUALIZE

Journey of Wonder

DRAW CONCLUSIONS
Sometimes authors give clues through what the characters say.

> Mama says Jenny is "up before the rooster." Roosters crow at dawn, so Jenny got up before dawn.

Papa gives Jenny clues to where they're going. List one clue.

At last, the big day had arrived. Jenny Burke pulled her bonnet over her brown curls, then raced to the kitchen. Her mother was stirring hot cereal over the fire in the hearth. "You're up before the rooster!" Mama said.

"Yes, Mama," Jenny replied. She was too excited to sleep. She was going on a trip with Papa. He had a surprise for her.

After breakfast, Papa and Jenny put blankets and food in the wagon. Then they set off.

"Where are we going, Papa?"

"I'll give you a hint," said Papa. "We're traveling north from Tonawanda, then west."

Three years ago, Jenny's family moved to Tonawanda, New York. Papa had a supply store near their cabin.

"Are we going to visit my cousins in Canada?"

"You'll find out soon enough," said Papa.

bonnet (BON-et) hat for women or girls
hearth (HARTH) fireplace

The wagon creaked along. The summer sun was hot. Papa and Jenny passed many orchards with apple and pear trees.

They came to a low bridge that crossed over a river. The bridge wasn't much wider than the wagon, and the sides were made of rope, not wood. It looked so rickety!

"Are we taking the wagon over *that*, Papa?" Jenny asked.

"We have to!" Papa said. "You'll have to get out of the wagon and walk."

Papa led the horses onto the shaky bridge. Jenny walked ahead of him, hanging on to the rope. She was sure the bridge would fall into the river. But it didn't.

By late afternoon, they reached Black Rock on the Niagara (ny-AG-ruh) River. They took a ferry across. Then they stopped at an inn for the night.

QUESTION

Ask yourself questions to make sure you know what's happening in a story.

How does Jenny feel about crossing the bridge? I can tell she is worried because she thinks the bridge will fall into the river.

Write another question you have about the story. Then write the answer.

creaked (KREEKT) squeaked
inn (IN) a hotel
rickety (RIK-uh-tee) weak or shaky

UNDERSTAND GENRE

(historical fiction)
Historical fiction uses some real facts from long ago. Write one fact that shows this story takes place in the past.

_____

_____

_____

VISUALIZE

As you read, use the words to make a picture of Niagara Falls in your mind.

I see _____

_____

_____

blacksmith (BLAK-smith) person who makes or fixes things made of iron, like horseshoes

guide (GIDE) person who shows the way

misty spray (MIS-tee SPRAY) tiny drops of water in the air

After dinner at the inn, they sat on the porch and felt a cool breeze in the air. Papa pointed to a misty spray in the distance. "Over there is your surprise."

He would not say more.

The next morning, a guide met them at the inn. He led them along a path near the Niagara River. Jenny heard a loud, powerful pounding. She thought of the town blacksmith hammering iron horseshoes. This sound was like a million blacksmiths hammering at once!

They climbed a high hill. They saw the river falling over a cliff shaped like a gigantic horseshoe. They saw the great Niagara Falls! A giant rainbow curved above the shaking, turning waters. Mist rose up and wet their faces.

Everything was so beautiful! Jenny turned to Papa and grinned. What a wonderful surprise!

Identify Plot

Stories have a beginning, a middle, and an end. Think about "Journey of Wonder." Use the story map below to write one more important event that happens in each part of the story. One important event is already filled in for each part. Go back to the story for ideas.

Title
_____

In the beginning

Jenny is excited about going on a trip with her father.
_____

In the middle

Jenny and Papa came to a bridge.
_____

Finally, in the end

A guide leads them to Niagara Falls.
_____

Summarize

A summary tells the most important events of a story.
Think about "Journey of Wonder." Choose the best summary below.
Use your story map on page 51 to help you decide.

(A) Jenny and her father go on a trip. The trip is a surprise. It is summer time. They have fun.

(B) Jenny was a girl who lived 200 years ago in Tonawanda, New York. Her father owned a store in the town. They had a cabin and a wagon. They crossed a bridge with their wagon.

(C) Jenny and her father leave their home in Tonawanda on a wagon trip. They travel west. They cross a rickety bridge and take a ferry. Then they visit Niagara Falls—a great surprise for Jenny.

I'll think about what the main characters (Jenny and her father) did in each part of the story—the beginning, middle, and end. That helps me decide the best summary.

Identify Sequence

Read page 50 again. Choose what you think are the four most important things that happen on the page. List them in order as they appear in that part of the story. The first one has been done for you.

1. **Papa pointed to a misty spray in the distance.** _____

2. _____

3. _____

4. _____

Jenny thought that Niagara Falls sounded like a million blacksmiths hammering away on horse shoes. What could cause that much noise? Read on and you'll find out.

Think About Genre

Historical fiction includes facts from the past, but the characters, actions, places, or events may be made up. That is why it is fiction. **Nonfiction** tells only about real people, real places, real actions, and real events.

Nonfiction can look different, too. An article may be divided into parts that have titles, or headings. These headings tell you what each part is about. Look at the **nonfiction article**, "Thunder of Water." Then answer these questions:

1. How many headings are there?

_____

2. How many photographs are there?

_____

3. Do you see: a graph? a chart? or a map?

_____

Think About the Topic

Read the introduction to "Thunder of Water" again. Then think about "Journey of Wonder." Write two things that you know about Niagara Falls.

1. _____

_____

2. _____

_____

Preview and Predict

You looked at the article, "Thunder of Water." Write one thing you expect to learn.

_____

_____

_____

STRATEGIES

**MAKE CONNECTIONS
UNDERSTAND GENRE
QUESTION**

MAKE CONNECTIONS

Authors try to connect new information with what you might know.

> The author uses the idea of bathtubs to explain how much water spills over Niagara Falls.

What else does the author compare Niagara Falls to?

_____

Describe a lake or river you have seen.

_____

_____

_____

> 📖
> **fresh water** (FRESH WA-tur) water that is not salty
> **gallons** (GAL-uns) a liquid measure

The Greatest Flow on Earth

Think about a million bathtubs full of water. Line up all those bathtubs, and they would reach from New York to Florida. Now think about all that water falling at once over a tall, wide cliff.

That's how much water spills over Niagara Falls every second. It adds up to about 37 million **gallons** of water per minute. No other waterfall on Earth has so much water flowing over it!

Niagara Falls is about 180 feet high. That's about as tall as a building with 16 floors. In the world, 50 waterfalls are higher. Only one other waterfall is wider. That is Victoria Falls in Africa.

Look at the map on page 55. These Great Lakes hold much of the world's **fresh water**. The water passes through Lake Erie, and then moves into the Niagara River—and over Niagara Falls.

Niagara Falls as seen from Canada

Sieur de La Salle, a French explorer, joined Father Hennepin in exploring Niagara Falls.

The five Great Lakes hold much of the world's fresh water.

Early History of Niagara Falls

The first people to visit Niagara Falls were the Native Americans. The word Niagara comes from the language of the Iroquois.

Early explorers heard stories about a great waterfall. Not many of them saw Niagara Falls. A French priest named Father Hennepin (HEN-uh-pin) was the first to write about what he saw. In 1678, he joined an explorer in Canada named Sieur de La Salle (SYUR DEH LAH SAHL).

When they reached the falls, Father Hennepin was scared. He wrote about a "horrible mass of water." He told about a "sound more terrible than that of thunder." People were amazed! His books sold very well.

After the American Revolution (1763–1783), more settlers arrived in western New York. They built roads along the Native American trails. Many tourists came to visit the wonderful waterfall.

UNDERSTAND GENRE
(article)
Nonfiction articles about history tell about events in the order they happened.

The part "Early History of Niagara Falls" begins with Native Americans, the first people to know about the falls.

What did an early explorer do to help more people learn about Niagara Falls?

_____

_____

_____

explorers (ek-SPLOR-ers) people who travel in a place that is not well known

Iroquois (EAR-uh-kwoy) Native American group who live in the region of Niagara Falls

tourists (TOOR-ists) sightseers

Why does water flow slower now? The power plants on the river take away some of the water's power.

Why has Niagara Falls moved?

_____

_____

_____

_____

Niagara Falls Today

Every year about 10 million tourists visit Niagara Falls. There are many hotels nearby. Boats bring visitors close to the bottom of the falls.

Time changes most things. For a while now, power plants have used the river's water to make electricity. This has caused the water to flow more slowly than it did years ago. The falls have also moved. They are about 2,000 feet farther back from where they were in Father Hennepin's time. That is because over the years water has eroded the rocky cliff.

Even with these changes, Niagara Falls has great beauty and power. It is still a natural wonder to people from all over the world!

Brave spectators view the base of the falls from a boat.

Believe It or Not

In 1860, Blondin, an acrobat, crossed the Niagara River near the falls on a tightrope. Later he put a stove out on the rope. Then he cooked a meal.

eroded (ee-ROHD-ed)
worn away

Identify Sequence

The last two parts of the article tell about events in the order they happened. They start with the heading "Early History of Niagara Falls," and end with "Niagara Falls Today."

Look at the chart below. It shows what happened over time. Complete the sentences to show the order of events. The last one has been done for you.

The Iroquois lived in and around New York.

Native Americans

_____ .

↓

In 1678, Father Hennepin and Sieur de la Salle

_____ .

↓

After the American Revolution in 1783,

_____ .

↓

Today, over 10 million tourists visit the Niagara Falls. Power plants use the river's water. The falls have moved. It still has great power and beauty, and is a natural wonder.

Summarize

When you finish reading an article, you may want to share it with a friend. A summary helps you do that. It should be short and clear. It tells in your own words what the article is about.

Summarize the section "Niagara Falls Today."

_____

_____

_____

_____

_____

Identify the Main Idea

The headings help you understand the most important information in each section of an article. The first heading is: "The Greatest Flow on Earth." Turn this heading into a question: *What is the Greatest Flow on Earth?* The answer to that question is the main idea of the section.

Turn the heading below into a question. Then answer the question.

A rainbow forms in the mist below the Niagara Falls.

Early History of Niagara Falls

Question: _____

Answer: _____

_____

Make Connections

Think about how "Journey of Wonder" and "Thunder of Water" connect to each other and to you.

1. Imagine that the character Jenny read the article. How might she describe the falls to her friends when she goes back home?

_____

_____

_____

2. How was the Niagara Falls Jenny saw in "Journey of Wonder" different from the way it is today?

_____

_____

3. Tell about a place you've read about or seen that has filled you with wonder.

_____

_____

The Grand Canyon is an American natural wonder.

Write a Descriptive Postcard

Pretend you are visiting Niagara Falls. Write a postcard to a friend. Write your feelings about being there. Use what you learned in both selections. If you have really been there, use your own experience to write about it.

 Before you write, use the *Greetings from Niagara Falls!* handout your teacher will give you to plan your postcard.

Plan Your Research

There are many natural wonders in the world, like the Grand Canyon, Mount Everest, and Niagara Falls. Choose one of these and write two questions you would like to have answered about the place.

1. _____

_____

2. _____

_____

They Are Patriots

In 1775, the American colonies belonged to Britain, but many Americans hoped to change that. In this historical fiction story, each person has to make a choice. Should they remain loyal to the king? Should they join the fight for independence?

Think About Genre

Historical fiction stories seem real and take place in the past. To make the story seem real, authors need to know a lot about how people lived during that time in history. Authors who write historical fiction always need to do research and use their imagination.

How do you know that "They Are Patriots" takes place in the past? Fill in the bubble beside the two sentences that tell you.

Ⓐ The characters' clothes and homes fit with that time in history.

Ⓑ Things happen in the story that could not happen in real life.

Ⓒ The story tells about events that really happened in history.

Think About the Topic

Read the above introduction to "They Are Patriots" again. Why did some people in the American colonies want to fight for independence?

_____

_____

Preview and Predict

Take a quick look at the story. Think about what you read in the introduction. What do you think the characters will argue about in "They Are Patriots"?

_____

_____

STRATEGIES

**DRAW CONCLUSIONS
QUESTION
VISUALIZE
UNDERSTAND GENRE**

They Are Patriots

DRAW CONCLUSIONS
Use clues in a story to help you figure out what is happening.

What were Ben and his father arguing about?

Mary heard her father and brother Ben arguing in the hall.

"I will not live with a traitor under my roof!" her father shouted.

"Then I will not be staying," replied Ben. With a slam of the door, he was gone.

Mary ran to her father. His face was red with anger. "Fight the British, indeed! That boy has lost his mind."

Mary knew Ben was meeting secretly with people who wanted to be free from Britain's control. Most of the men of their town, Concord, Massachusetts, were on her brother's side. They called themselves Patriots.

Mary's father was not one of them. He was loyal to the King of Britain.

"Has Ben left us for good?" asked Mary.

"I hope not," her father sighed. "Perhaps he'll come home soon."

Patriot (PAY-tree-ut) supporter of independence from British rule

traitor (TRAY-tur) a person who helps an enemy of his or her own country

Mary thought Ben was right. But she didn't think she should say so.

Then, on April 19, 1775, British troops marched out of Boston. They shot and killed Patriots in Lexington and at the North Bridge in Concord.

"This is terrible!" her father roared. "I may soon have to join the Patriots!"

Mary was glad to hear his words. She tried very hard to bring her father over to the Patriots' side.

The town was buzzing with news. The American colonies had joined together to form a Continental Congress. At meetings of this Congress, leaders decided what to do.

Mary listened to all the news. Every day she told her father something bad about the British. Finally, one day in June, her words made a difference.

QUESTION
Ask yourself questions when you wonder about ideas or events. Reread or read ahead to find answers.

I wonder, "Why does Mary keep her thoughts to herself?"

Why do you think she does?

colonies (KAHL-uh-neez) settlements that are far from the nation that rules them

VISUALIZE
Use words to help you imagine characters.

Which words help you picture George Washington?

UNDERSTAND GENRE
(historical fiction)
Some events in this story really happened. Write two historical events that led Mary's father to change his mind.

1. _____

_____

2. _____

_____

📖

commander-in-chief
(kuh-MAN-dur-in-cheef) the person who is in charge at the highest level

Mary knew how much her father looked up to George Washington. Twenty years earlier, they had fought together against the French.

"The Continental Congress named George Washington the **commander-in-chief** of a new Continental Army," Mary told her father. "He is coming here to help force the British out of Boston!"

Mary's father was convinced at last.

On July 2, George Washington took command of the army outside Boston. Mary and her father went to Cambridge to see him gallop by. As the tall, handsome man in a blue uniform rode by on his large white horse, people cheered.

Suddenly, Mary heard a voice she knew. She turned, and there was Ben! Mary ran to him and yelled that their father was now a Patriot. "You can come home again, Ben!" Mary cried.

They Are Patriots

Identify Parts of a Story

Think about the parts that make up this story.

Look back at "They Are Patriots" to find the information you need to complete this chart.

Characters

_____

_____

Setting

time _____

place _____

Problem

Father is loyal to Britain, but Ben and Mary want him to join the Patriots.

Important Events

_____

_____

_____

Conclusion

_____

They Are Patriots

Summarize

Think about how one of the characters might tell the story. How would Ben tell it? Write a summary as if you are Ben. Remember to use the word "I" in your summary.

I'll imagine that I am Ben. I'll tell why I left home, what the British did, what my sister did, and how my father changed his mind.

_____

_____

_____

_____

_____

Identify Cause and Effect

A cause is the reason why something happens. An effect is what happens. Read each effect in the chart below. Then write the cause, or reason why it happened.

Why It Happened

What Happened

1. _____

1. Ben and his father had an argument.

2. _____

2. Mary's father looked up to George Washington.

George ★★★★★★ Washington ★★★★★★★★★★★★

Who is that man on the one-dollar bill? And why is his picture there? Find out about the man we call the "Father of His Country."

Think About Genre

The story of a real person's life is called a **biography** (by-AHG-ruh-fee). It tells about a person and some events that happened in his or her life. A biography is just one kind of **nonfiction**.

Look at the pictures in this short biography of George Washington. What events in his life are included in the biography?

_____

_____

_____

Think About the Topic

Reread the introduction to "George Washington." Ask yourself: *What did I learn about George Washington from reading "They Are Patriots"?* Write something you know about him.

_____

_____

_____

Preview and Predict

Now that you have read the title and looked at the biography, make a prediction. Write one question you expect to answer by reading this short biography, "George Washington."

_____

_____

STRATEGIES

DRAW CONCLUSIONS
QUESTION
UNDERSTAND GENRE

George ★★★★★★
Washington
★★★★★★★★★★★★★

George's Family

George Washington was born in 1732 and grew up in the British colony of Virginia. The oldest of five children, George had one sister and three brothers. He also had two older half-brothers from his father's first marriage.

George was only 11 years old when his father died, but his half-brother Lawrence became like a father to him. George often visited Lawrence at his home, a farm called Mount Vernon. When he was 16, George moved to Mount Vernon, a home he would one day own.

DRAW CONCLUSIONS
Why did George decide to move to Mount Vernon?

_____

_____

_____

_____

_____

_____

Joining the Army

George joined the Virginia militia in 1752. He was 20 years old. By 1753, Britain and France were disagreeing about who would control North America. Both countries had colonists there. The French people in the Ohio Valley area did not want the British to settle there, too. The British disagreed with the French. When a war finally started between the two countries, George Washington fought for the British. The leaders of the army noticed George's skill and gave him a more important position. It was the start of a successful military career.

military career (MIL-uh-tehr-ee kuh-REER) earning a living as a soldier

militia (muh-LISH-uh) an army of regular citizens

George's home after age 16 at Mount Vernon

George's marriage to Martha

Getting Married

In 1759, when George was 26, he married Martha Dandridge Custis. Martha had two young children. Her first husband, a successful farmer from Virginia, had left her 17,000 acres of land when he died. By getting married, Martha and George became a wealthy family. George had left the military and was happy to be home at Mount Vernon with his family.

Leading the Continental Army

In the years after the war with France, many colonists became unhappy living under British rule. They resented the taxes that the British demanded from them. The British also expected the colonists to sell their crops only to Britain and to buy all their supplies from Britain. The colonists felt these rules were unfair.

By 1775, the colonists wanted independence from the British government. On April 19, British troops arrived at the towns of Lexington and Concord. The colonists and the British fought battles there. In May, the colonists formed the Continental Army. Because of his military experience, George Washington was chosen as commander-in-chief of the new army.

QUESTION
Remember to ask yourself questions to help you understand new information.

Write a question you have about something on this page. Circle the answer when you find it.

_____

_____

_____

_____

_____

_____

resented (ree-ZENT-id) felt angry about
taxes (TAKS-is) money people pay to the government

elected (EE-lekt-id) voted into office

George led the army throughout the American Revolution. In 1781, the British surrendered and the colonists finally won the war.

President Washington

In 1789, Washington became the nation's first president. He is the only president to have been chosen by every single voter. Unlike any other government at that time, the new government would be led by elected leaders to serve the American people. Washington was elected president twice. He finished his second term in 1797.

George Washington became sick and died in 1799 after riding his horse around Mount Vernon during a storm. After his death, General Henry Lee wrote that Washington was "first in war, first in peace, and first in the hearts of his countrymen."

Today, Washington is famous for being the first president of the United States. An honest and quiet man, he never expected to be a famous president. Always willing to serve when his country needed him, George Washington is one of our greatest leaders.

Identify Sequence

Use the time line below to list important events in George Washington's life. Be sure to put the events in time order. Find the 6 events (including his birth) that you think are most important. One has been done for you.

1732 _____

_____

1753 _____

_____

1759 _____

_____

1775 _____

_____

1789 _____

_____

1799 **Washington dies**

On April 14, 1789, Washington found out that he was elected president. But what were people to call the new president? Some suggested "His Highness" or "His Excellence." Lawmakers settled on "Mr. President."

George ★★★★★★
Washington
★★★★★★★★★★★★

Summarize

If someone from another country asked you about George Washington, what would you tell him or her?
   In a few sentences, tell the most important facts about this man.

I will look at the headings to help me decide what the most important ideas are.

_____

_____

_____

_____

Identify Details

A biography includes many facts about a person's life. On the line after each fact below, tell why it was important in George Washington's life. Look back over the biography to help you write your answers.

George Washington felt a strong duty to help his country.

1. In 1753, Britain and France were about to go to war.

_____

_____

2. When British soldiers battled with colonists in Lexington and Concord in 1775, the war began.

_____

_____

They Are Patriots

George ★★★★★★
Washington
★★★★★★★★★★★

Make Connections

Think about "They Are Patriots" and "George Washington." Answer the questions to connect the selections to each other and to you.

1. In the story, Mary's father looked up to George Washington. How would her father describe him? Use what you learned about George Washington in the biography.

_____

_____

_____

2. Which two details were the same in both the story and the biography?

_____

_____

_____

Statue of President George Washington in the George Washington Memorial in Alexandria, Virginia

3. George Washington was one kind of a leader. What do you think a good leader does?

_____

_____

_____

Write About an Event

The day George Washington became president was a special event in his life. Write about the day as if you were George Washington. Describe what you saw, felt, and heard.

_____

_____

_____

_____

 Before you write, use the *By George!* handout your teacher will give you to plan your event.

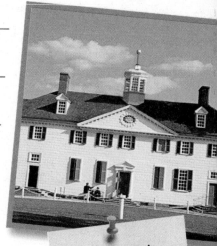

Mount Vernon is in the state of Virginia.

Plan Your Research

What else would you like to learn about George Washington or the American colonies? Write two questions you would like to have answered.

1. _____

_____

2. _____

_____

Tears and Dreams

Picture yourself moving to a new country. Do you think it could be exciting? In this story, one boy's move turns out to be much harder than he had ever dreamed.

Think About Genre

Historical fiction is one type of **fiction**. In this kind of story, the characters are made up, but they seem real. Some of the events are part of history.

The story "Tears and Dreams" is historical fiction. What will you find in the story? Put an **X** next to the three answers.

_____ boats that talk

_____ an event that happens in 2093

_____ real places

_____ characters who seem real

_____ an event that happend almost one hundred years ago

Think About the Topic

Reread the introduction above. Ask yourself: *What would it be like to move to a new land?* Complete the word web.

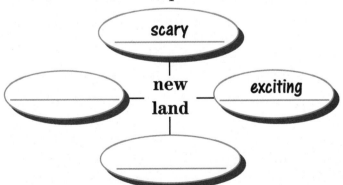

scary

new land

exciting

Preview and Predict

Look through the story. Think about the introduction and the illustrations. Complete the sentence.

I think this story will be about

_____

_____ .

STRATEGIES

VISUALIZE
MAKE CONNECTIONS
UNDERSTAND GENRE
MAKE INFERENCES

Tears and Dreams

March 5, 1912

Chen Hung stood on the main deck of the *Golden Eagle*. He had come all the way from Canton, China. At last, the ship entered San Francisco Harbor.

"Isn't the harbor beautiful?" Chen asked his friend, Long Lee.

"It's prettier than I dreamed," Long answered.

"I thought I'd never see the sun again," Chen said.

"Or smell the fresh air," Long added.

Until this morning, Chen had been living on the ship's lower deck. The deck was dark and wet.

The 30-day trip had been hard. Many men got sick. Some days they had no food.

Chen missed his family during the whole trip. He was alone and the youngest boy on the ship.

Today, he would see his uncle. Chen's uncle had a place where he could stay. He also had a job waiting for Chen. Chen planned to send money back to his family. That's why he came to America.

The ship pulled up to a dock. "We're almost there!" said Long excitedly.

"We will never forget this day!" Chen exclaimed.

"Never!" they repeated together.

VISUALIZE
Use the author's words to make pictures in your mind. These mind pictures will help you "see" what is happening in the story.

I can picture in my mind what it was like on the lower deck.

Picture Chen on the lower deck. Tell what you "see."

A Few Hours Later . . .

Chen found himself waiting in a crowded room. All the men from the lower deck were there, too. They carried everything they owned in packages that were tied to the ends of long poles. They whispered quietly.

No women were in sight. Mostly, the men from China came without their wives or children. The men were all here to earn money.

When Chen was on the ship, he imagined his uncle would meet him right away. They would go straight to his new home in San Francisco. That was his dream. But that was not what happened.

"Come this way!" shouted an official.

The crowd of men followed him. Soon they were back at the harbor. They all boarded boats.

"Where are we going?" Chen asked an older man he had met on the *Golden Eagle*.

"They are taking us to Angel Island. They will look over our papers there. Then they will let us enter San Francisco," he said. "I hope."

MAKE CONNECTIONS

The author doesn't tell you how Chen feels. Put yourself in his place. How would you feel?

Poor Chen! He's been on the ship for 30 days. Now he has to wait even longer. I would be so disappointed.

Write about a time you were disappointed like Chen.

official (uh-FISH-uhl) a person in charge

UNDERSTAND GENRE
(historical fiction)
The following story details are facts from history:
- stack of three bunks
- 100 men in the barracks
- writing on the walls

Write one other detail that might be a fact.

MAKE INFERENCES
Sometimes you have to use details in a story and what you know to figure out what's happening.

Why would doctors give the men a check-up before they could enter San Francisco?

barracks (BEHR-uks)
a building or many buildings where large groups of people live

Three Days Later . . .

Chen sat on the lower bunk in a large room. Over his bunk were two more bunks. In all, 100 men, mostly from China, lived in the crowded room.

Chen was glad that he would see his uncle today. The past three days had been very hard.

Doctors gave Chen a complete check-up. Officials asked him many questions. He was scared all the time.

Chen's friend Long sat next to him. Like Chen, Long was meeting *his* uncle today. "Angel Island has been terrible," Chen said, sadly.

"Yes," Long agreed, "but still we are lucky."

On Angel Island, Chen had met men who were waiting for weeks and even months. Many had written their thoughts on the walls. Chen read them.

"I'll never, ever forget my stay here," said Chen.

"NEVER!" Chen and Long repeated together.

English words for Chinese writing on a wall at Angel Island.
I left Canton with a package of dreams.
I carried my dreams on a pole across the sea.
I saw the land of hope, but could not enter.
I shed tears on the Island of Angels.
There, I lost my package of dreams.

Understand Characters

In "Tears and Dreams," we learn about the kind of person Chen Hung is by what he says and what he does. A character has traits that help you know what he or she is like. Use the character chart below to help you understand Chen Hung. Read each character trait in the chart. Then find evidence from the story that shows each trait. Write it on the lines next to the trait.

Chen Hung Character Chart

Character Trait	Evidence
1. brave	1. _____ _____
2. unselfish	2. plans to send money back home
3. patient	3. _____ _____
4. caring	4. _____ _____

Summarize

A story summary tells only the main points of a story. Sometimes you can summarize a story by describing the character and the most important things that happen to him or her.

Write a summary of "Tears and Dreams." Use the character chart on page 79 to help you explain what happened to Chen Hung.

First, I'll write about who Chen Hung is and where he is going. Then I'll explain what he is like and what happens to him.

_____

_____

_____

_____

Identify Details

A story summary should include important details and leave out less important ones. Underline the most important detail of each section of the story.

Section 1: March 5, 1912
Chen stood on the main deck of the boat. Chen came to America to earn money for his family.

Section 2: A Few Hours Later . . .
Chen went to Angel Island first, not to his uncle's house. Chen asked an older friend a question.

Section 3: Three Days Later . . .
Chen knew he was lucky, even though he had a hard time at Angel Island.
Chen sat on the bunk with his friend.

ELLIS and ANGEL: Islands of Hope

Chen Hung entered the United States through Angel Island in California. How might his experience have been different if he had come through Ellis Island in New York? Read this article to find out.

Think About Genre

Some **nonfiction articles** about history compare and contrast information. They may compare and contrast people, places, or things.

What does it mean to compare two things?

_____

_____

_____

What does it mean to contrast two things?

_____

_____

_____

Think About the Topic

Reread the introduction to "Ellis and Angel: Islands of Hope." Write one thing you learned about Angel Island in "Tears and Dreams."

_____

_____

Preview and Predict

This article compares and contrasts Ellis Island and Angel Island. Preview the headings and photos. Write two things you think will be compared.

1. _____

_____

2. _____

_____

STRATEGIES

MAKE INFERENCES
UNDERSTAND GENRE
QUESTION

MAKE INFERENCES

Authors don't always tell you everything. Sometimes they give you clues and you have to use what you know to figure out something.

Why would the U.S. government begin to set limits on how many people could come to America?

_____

_____

_____

coast (KOHST) land along the sea

ferry (FEHR-ee) a boat that carries people and cars

immigration (im-ih-GRAY-shun) movement of people to a new land

ELLIS and ANGEL: Islands of Hope

Starting New Lives

The year is 1910. A young girl from Germany has been at the immigration center on Ellis Island for five days. Doctors have given her a complete check-up. Officials have asked her questions.

At last, she boards a boat for New York City. The girl waves to Lady Liberty, the great statue in New York Harbor. She and her family will start a new life in America.

Meanwhile, on the west coast of the United States, a teenaged Chinese boy waits for a ferry. He is finally leaving Angel Island in San Francisco Bay. The boy has been at the immigration station there for three weeks. Tomorrow he will begin working. He plans to send money to help his family back in China.

Land of Immigrants

The United States is a land with many immigrants. Some families have just arrived from faraway places. Other families settled here a long time ago.

For many years, anyone could come to America. Then, after awhile, the United States government began to set limits.

Young immigrants waiting for medical exams before entering the United States

Ellis Island Immigration Center

In 1892, an immigration center opened on Ellis Island in New York Harbor.

Ships landing in the harbor carried many passengers, both rich and poor. Most rich passengers entered the United States quickly. Most poor passengers went by boat or barge to Ellis Island.

Days on Ellis Island

Most people stayed four or five days on Ellis Island. They had to fill out forms. Inspectors asked them many questions. Doctors checked their health. After that, most immigrants could enter the country. Some, about one in 50 people, were sent back to their home country.

The center was open until 1954. During that time, 12 million people entered the United States through Ellis Island.

Ellis Island Today

In 1965, Ellis Island became part of the Liberty National Monument. Today, the main building is the Ellis Island Immigration Museum. About two million people visit this historic place each year.

© Options Publishing. No copying permitted.

UNDERSTAND GENRE
(nonfiction article)
The article compares and contrasts Ellis Island to Angel Island. This part of the article tells about Ellis Island. There are three headings. Each heading tells what you will be reading about. Write what each part is about.

Part 1: _____

_____

Part 2: _____

_____

Part 3: _____

_____

barge (BARJ) a large, flat boat towed by another boat
inspectors (in-SPEK-turs) people who carefully look at someone or something
monument (MON-yoo-munt) something put up in memory of someone or something

Angel Island Immigration Center

In 1910, another United States immigration station opened. This one was in San Francisco Bay, on Angel Island. Some people called it the "Ellis Island of the West."

Inspection Process

Angel Island became a detention center for Chinese immigrants. Most people were kept on the island for two to three weeks. Many stayed for months or even years.

They lived in crowded places. Most immigrants did not speak English. Officials asked them many questions. Being at the island could be very confusing. About one out of four Chinese immigrants was not allowed into the United States.

In 30 years, more than 250,000 immigrants passed through Angel Island. Most of them were Asians.

Angel Island Today

Immigrants no longer enter through Angel Island. Today, there is a museum in the old station. Visitors come to read poems that immigrants wrote on the walls. They come to learn the story of America's Asian immigrants.

Asians (AY-zhuns) people from Asia

detention (dee-TEN-shun) a holding area, like a jail

Angel Island

Ellis Island

ELLIS and ANGEL:
Islands of Hope

Compare and Contrast

This article compares and contrasts Ellis Island to Angel Island. It explains how the two immigration centers were alike and different.
   Use what you learned about both places to complete the chart.

Ellis Island	Angel Island

Alike

1. Officials asked questions in both places.

2. Immigrants were sent back home from both places.

3. _____

4. _____

Different

1. opened in 1892

2. 1 in 50 sent back

3. _____

   _____

4. _____

Different

1. opened in 1910

2. 1 in 4 sent back

3. _____

   _____

4. _____

ELLIS and ANGEL:
Islands of Hope

Summarize

Summarizing is a good way to check your memory. It is also a good way to see how much you understand.

Summarize the information in "Ellis and Angel: Islands of Hope." Use the compare-and-contrast chart on page 85 to help you.

_____

_____

_____

> I will start my summary by telling what two places are being compared and contrasted. Next, I'll tell how the two centers were alike. Then, I'll describe their differences.

_____

_____

_____

_____

_____

Identify the Main Idea

The headings of each section tell you what is important in that section. If you turn the heading into a question, it will lead you to the main idea of the section. Underline the heading in each question below.

1. What was Ellis Island Immigration Center like?

2. What is the land of immigrants?

3. What was the inspection process?

4. What is Angel Island like today?

Make Connections

Think about how the two selections connect to each other and to you.

1. How was Chen's story like the story of the Chinese boy in the first section of the nonfiction article? How was it different?

Alike: _____

_____

Different: _____

_____

2. Would Chen still have moved to the United States if he had read the article before leaving China? Tell why or why not.

_____

_____

3. Tell about someone you know or have read about who has moved to a new place. How did he or she feel?

_____

_____

_____

Immigrants traveling by boat to America

Write a Journal Entry

It's 1920. Suppose you just arrived at Ellis Island or Angel Island with your family. Write a journal entry about your experience. Explain what you see, hear, smell, and feel. Tell what happens.

_____

_____

_____

_____

_____

_____

_____

 Before you write, use the *I'm Here!* handout your teacher will give you to plan your journal entry.

Plan Your Research

Chen Hung's homeland of China has many amazing places. Find out about one part of China, such as Canton, Hong Kong, or Beijing. Write two questions you would like to research.

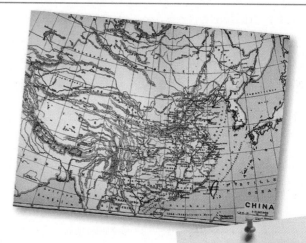

Map of China, where Canton, Hong Kong, and Beijing are located

1. _____

_____

2. _____

_____

What would you expect from a visit to the attic? Possibly a treasure hunt? It may become a trip to the past and a time to learn about people you love! In this story, a visit to the attic is all of those things.

Think About Genre

In **realistic fiction** stories, the author makes the story seem real. The characters are made up, but they are like people you might meet. The places could also be real.

What do you expect to find in realistic fiction? Put an **X** next to two sentences.

_____ The characters could live in your town.

_____ The place seems real.

_____ The characters are talking birds.

_____ You will read only facts.

Think About the Topic

Read the introduction to "Attic Stardust" again. Write two things you might find in an attic.

1. _____

2. _____

Preview and Predict

Look at the title and pictures and read the first paragraph. Check the box next to the words that best finish the sentence below.

In this story, a boy finds something in the attic that

☐ he can eat.

☐ he can read.

☐ he can use in baseball.

STRATEGIES

QUESTION
DRAW CONCLUSIONS
UNDERSTAND GENRE
VISUALIZE

QUESTION
Remember to ask yourself questions as you read.

What does Mom mean when she says, "Our attic is full of memories"?

memories (MEM-uh-reez) things that are remembered

Attic Stardust

Early one morning, Marcus followed his mother up the stairway to the attic. Boxes, furniture, and old toys filled the room. "Our attic is full of memories," Mom said.

Mom had promised Marcus a reward for writing a prize-winning story. His class was supposed to write a story about the past. There would be a prize for the best story.

"You can look through two boxes today, Marcus," Mom said, as she went off to another corner of the attic. Marcus was hoping to find a pack of baseball cards that his father had put away a long time ago. Maybe this would be his lucky day. He closed his eyes and picked two boxes.

The first one was filled with some old roller-skates. He opened the second box. There, on top, were some pictures of a young woman he didn't know. Under the pictures were some letters, books, and notebooks.

"Who is this, Mom?" he asked.

Mom stood over the box. "That's Grandma," Mom said.

"It doesn't look like Grandma. Is this her journal?" Marcus asked, holding up a notebook.

Mom picked it up and looked inside. "Yes, this journal has some of Grandma's first stories."

Then Mom picked up another book. The cover said *Dust Tracks on a Road*. "This was one of Grandma's favorite books. It's by an author named Zora Neale Hurston."

"Who?" Marcus asked.

"Zora Neale Hurston, an African-American woman who was born over 100 years ago," Mom said. "She was quite a writer, and an amazing woman, too."

"What do you mean?" Marcus asked.

"It was almost impossible for an African-American woman to become a famous writer in those days," Mom said. "You need to ask Grandma about her. She can tell you a lot more than I can."

DRAW CONCLUSIONS

Authors don't always tell you everything. Use clues in a story to figure out what is happening.

How do you know that Grandma is a writer?

Why can Marcus' grandma tell him more about Zora Neale Hurston?

UNDERSTAND GENRE
(realistic fiction)
Details about a place make the story seem real. For example, there were boxes, furniture, and toys in the attic.

What is another detail that makes the story seem real?

VISUALIZE
Details can help you "see" the characters in your mind.

Write a detail that helps you "see" Grandma in your mind.

education (ej-uh-KAY-shun) knowledge gained by learning; schooling

That afternoon, Marcus walked into Grandma's apartment. "What do you have there?" Grandma asked.

Marcus held up the journal and the book he had found in the attic. Grandma's big eyes got even bigger as she smiled. "Zora Neale Hurston was my hero!" she exclaimed.

"Why was she your hero, Grandma?" he asked.

"Zora Neale Hurston lived quite a life," Grandma said. Her eyes flashed with excitement. "By the time she was 13, her mother had died and Zora was alone. Even so, she got an education and became a writer."

"That must've been hard," Marcus said.

"Very hard. After I read Zora's book about her life, I decided I could become a writer, too."

Marcus walked over to Grandma's bookcase. She had written most of the children's books on her shelf. Marcus was very proud of his grandma.

"I want to be a writer someday, too," he said. "You can be a writer," Grandma said. "You know what Zora Neale Hurston's mom used to tell her?"

"What?"

"She always said, 'Jump at the sun.' She meant that you can do whatever you set your mind to. So, Marcus, just remember that, and you, too, will get whatever you set your mind to."

Attic Stardust

Identify Setting and Plot

Story settings help the reader get a picture of where and when a story takes place. This story has two settings. The plot is what happens in a story. Complete the charts below.

First Setting

When (time): _____

Where (place): the attic _____

Plot

What happens: _____

_____

Second Setting

When (time): _____

Where (place): _____

Plot

Marcus and Grandma talk about Zora Neale Hurston

and writing.

Summarize

Write a short summary of "Attic Stardust." Use what you learned about the settings to help you retell the story. The charts on page 93 can also help you. Write about two things that happened in each setting.

_____

_____

_____

_____

_____

_____

_____

Identify Details

Some details in a story are more important than others. They are important for understanding what the story is mostly about. Put a check next to the two most important details.

_____ Grandma told Marcus about Zora Neale Hurston.

_____ Grandma had a bookshelf.

_____ Marcus opened a box that had skates in it.

_____ Marcus is a boy.

_____ Marcus learned a lot about Grandma's life.

Why does a person become a writer? Read this biography to find out about one writer from Eatonville, Florida.

Think About Genre

In "Attic Stardust," Mom and Grandma are made-up characters. However, they both tell facts about Zora Neale Hurston—a real person. The type of **nonfiction** you are about to read is a **biography** of Zora Neale Hurston. A biography tells about a real person's life.

Look through this biography. Look at the headings and pictures. Then answer **yes** or **no** to each of the following questions.

_____ Does this biography tell about different parts of Zora Neale Hurston's life?

_____ Does it tell about her family?

_____ Does it tell about authors of the future?

_____ Does it show what she looked like?

Think About the Topic

Remember what you read about Zora Neale Hurston in "Attic Stardust." Answer each question below.

1. What did you learn about her?

_____

_____

2. What would you like to learn?

_____

Preview and Predict

Look at the story headings again. They describe parts of Zora Neale Hurston's life. Check the box next to two headings that help you predict her life was not easy.

☐ The Busy Hurston Home

☐ Early Struggles

☐ The Harlem Renaissance

☐ A Writer's Struggle

STRATEGIES

**MAKE CONNECTIONS
UNDERSTAND GENRE
QUESTION**

Zora Neale Hurston

The Busy Hurston Home

Born in 1891, Zora Neale Hurston was number seven of eight children. There were six boys and two girls. The Hurston home was always noisy. Friends and visitors were always around.

Zora's father was the mayor of their town, Eatonville, Florida. It was the first African-American town in America run by African Americans. About 300 people lived there.

Zora Neale Hurston

Zora's favorite spot in Eatonville was Joe Clark's store. Men gathered at the store to tell stories. Zora spent much time there listening. She learned a lot about storytelling.

Zora didn't get along well with her father. He didn't like her spirit. She didn't always listen to him. He told her not to read books. She read everything in sight. He didn't like poets. She said she was going to be a poet one day.

Zora's mother listened to her stories. She defended Zora. She encouraged her to "jump at the sun."

MAKE CONNECTIONS
Think about where you read "jump at the sun" before.

I read it in "Attic Stardust." Grandma explained it to Marcus.

Use what you learned in the story to tell what "jump at the sun" means.

_____

_____

_____

defended (dih-FEND-id) kept safe from harm

encouraged (en-KUR-ijd) gave hope to

spirit (SPEER-it) liveliness; courage

Early Struggles

Zora's life changed when she was 13 years old. In 1904, her mother died. Two weeks later, her father sent her away to a boarding school.

Then Zora's father got married again. Zora's new stepmother didn't like her stepchildren.

Soon Zora was out of school and living on her own. She joined a traveling opera show and worked for an actress. She read many books. She realized that she wanted to write.

Getting an education was a huge struggle. She had no money. She had no help from her family. She did have something else, though. Zora Neale Hurston was very smart. And she had spirit.

The Harlem Renaissance

By 1925, Zora was living in a part of New York City called Harlem. Many African Americans lived in Harlem in the 1920s. It was an exciting time when people came together to make music, write books and poetry, and create works of art. It was a new time for African Americans. They were part of the "Harlem Renaissance" (REN-uh-sahns).

A jazz club in Harlem

boarding school
(BORD-ing SKOOL) school away from home where students pay to learn

Harlem Renaissance
a time when much art, literature, and music was produced by African Americans living in Harlem

struggle (STRUG-ul)
something hard to do

Ask yourself questions to help you understand new information.

Write a question about what you have read.

_____

_____

_____

_____

Write a question that you would ask Zora about her life if you could.

_____

_____

_____

_____

fame (FAYM) the condition of being well-known; popular

A Writer's Struggle

Zora struggled her whole life to earn a living. She earned some fame, but she never made much money.

Many times Zora worked at different jobs. She worked as a waitress. She worked in a library. She taught school, and she cleaned houses.

Through it all, Zora wrote and traveled. She published many books, short stories, and plays. She had a lot to say about the lives of African Americans.

Zora Neale Hurston died in 1960. Her life was hard, but she always tried to "jump at the sun."

Stars of the Harlem Renaissance

★ Bessie Smith, singer

★ Langston Hughes, poet

★ Duke Ellington, musician

Identify Sequence

This biography is written in time order. It starts when Zora is a child and ends when she dies.

The organizer below is a timeline. It shows the time order of events. Look back at the headings in the biography to help you figure out when things happened. Write each event and the date it happened in the boxes.

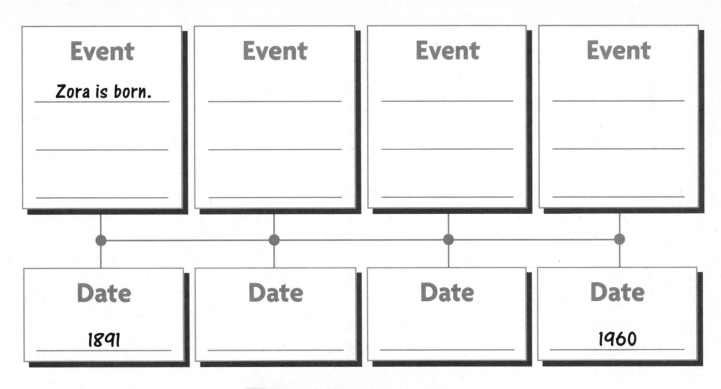

Event	**Event**	**Event**	**Event**
Zora is born.			

Date	**Date**	**Date**	**Date**
1891			1960

Zora Neale Hurston overcame difficulties to become a successful writer.

Summarize

Your friends may not know about Zora Neale Hurston. What important things would you tell them about her?

Write a summary of her life. Include dates and events from the time line on page 99.

_____

_____

_____

_____

_____

Identify Supporting Details

Details tell more about a main idea. Read each idea below from the biography. Fill in the bubble next to the detail that tells more about the main idea.

1. Zora worked at different jobs.

   Ⓐ Sometimes she worked as a waitress or a teacher.

   Ⓑ Zora wrote and liked to travel.

2. Many talented people were part of the Harlem Renaissance.

   Ⓐ Some singers lived in New York City.

   Ⓑ Writers, singers, and poets came together in Harlem in the 1920s.

Many of Zora Neale Hurston's books are read today.

Make Connections

Remember what you learned about Zora Neale Hurston from both selections. Answer the following questions.

1. What is one way Marcus and Zora Neale Hurston are the same and one way they are different?

Same: _____

_____

Different: _____

_____

2. How do you think Marcus would feel after reading the biography "Zora Neale Hurston"?

_____

_____

_____

3. In "Attic Stardust," Grandma called Zora Neale Hurston her hero. Who is your hero? Explain why.

_____

_____

_____

Write Interview Questions

Authors sometimes interview people before they write a biography. Choose a classmate or family member you would like to interview. Write three questions you would like to ask about the person's life.

1. _____

2. _____

3. _____

 Before you write, use the *Tell Me About Yourself* handout your teacher will give you to plan your interview questions.

Plan Your Research

The writer Langston Hughes was a friend of Zora Neale Hurston.

Choose one "star" from page 98. Write three things you would like to learn about him or her.

1. _____

_____

2. _____

_____

3. _____

_____

A Mammoth Adventure

By studying their bones, scientists have learned a lot about huge, furry beasts called mammoths. These gigantic animals died thousands of years ago. Could someone living today ever hope to see one alive?

Think About Genre

Fantasy stories are make-believe. In this **time-travel fantasy,** something happens that could never happen in real life. Yet, some parts seem real. The characters look and act like real people. The setting may be a real place. So, how do you know if a story is a fantasy? Just ask yourself, "Could these things really happen?" If not, you know the story is a fantasy.

Think about a fantasy story you have heard or read. Write its title on line 1. On line 2, write one thing that happened in the story that could not happen in real life.

1. _____

2. _____

_____

_____

Think About the Topic

Read the introduction to "A Mammoth Adventure" again. What does it tell you about mammoths? Write one idea on the lines below.

_____

_____

_____

Preview and Predict

Titles can give a clue about the story. Write a prediction of what this story will be about.

_____

_____

_____

STRATEGIES

QUESTION
VISUALIZE
UNDERSTAND GENRE
DRAW CONCLUSIONS

A Mammoth Adventure

QUESTION
Remember to ask yourself questions about the story.

I wonder why Liz and Ray are visiting Hot Springs, South Dakota?

What is the "real thing" they might find in Hot Springs?

"Wow!" said Liz, looking up at a huge skeleton. "Don't you wish you could see the real thing?"

"That's why I begged mom to bring us here," said Ray. "I've always wanted to see a real mammoth. Too bad they are extinct."

Liz and Ray were at a museum in Hot Springs, South Dakota. The trip was Ray's idea. He was writing a school report about mammoths. Many mammoth bones have been found in Hot Springs.

"There used to be a very big pool of hot water here," Ray told his sister. "The water was warm all year round. Animals came to the pool to drink, but they couldn't get out. The sides were too steep. It was a death trap!"

"Where is the water now?" asked Liz.

extinct (ek-STINGKT) no longer living anywhere in the world
steep (STEEP) slant sharply

"Long gone!" said Ray. "The pool slowly filled up with dirt. The bones of the trapped animals were hidden under all that dirt for 26,000 years! Now people are beginning to dig them out."

Later, Ray showed Liz a poster he was making for his school project. On it was a timeline and a pointer.

"This is a timeline," he explained. "It shows what happened to the mammoths through the years."

"Oh, here's when the mammoths died in the water," said Liz as she moved the pointer to 26,000 years ago. Ray had put a mammoth sticker there to mark it.

As soon as the pointer touched the sticker, something very strange happened. The sticker seemed to come alive! Suddenly there was a rush of cold wind. Then the museum disappeared! Ray and Liz were now standing on a grassy hill! And there were patches of snow on the ground!

As they turned, they saw a gigantic, furry beast. It looked like an elephant, but it had long, brown fur and huge, sharp tusks that were curved at the ends.

Liz and Ray backed away very slowly.

"Luckily, w-w-woolly mammoths d-d-don't eat m-m-meat!" stammered Ray.

VISUALIZE
Words can help you imagine a scene. Which words help you "see" what's happening in the story?

tusks (TUSKS) very long, pointed teeth of animals like the elephant

UNDERSTAND GENRE

(time-travel fantasy)
This story has parts that seem real and parts that are fantasy. Write one example of each.

Real: _____

_____

Fantasy: _____

_____

DRAW CONCLUSIONS

Why did Ray draw a line in the snow? Circle the letter of the correct answer.

a. to separate them from the bear

b. to make a timeline to get them back to the present

c. to explain to Liz where they were

Ice Age (ICE AYJ) a time long ago when most of Earth was covered with ice

"Where are we?" asked Liz.

"We must have traveled back in time to the Ice Age," said Ray. "I guess my wish came true. I'm seeing a real mammoth!"

Suddenly Liz looked really scared. All she could do was point at an animal coming over the snowy hill.

"Oh, no!" yelled Ray. "That giant bear definitely is a meat eater!"

"And it's coming this way!" cried Liz.

Quickly, Ray picked up a stick and drew a line in the snow. He pulled Liz onto the line with him. Then, as fast as he could, Ray wrote the word NOW where the line ended. Just in time! There was another rush of wind.

"Oh, there you are!" said their mother. "For a minute, I thought you two had disappeared."

Later that day, Ray still felt dizzy. He and Liz were in a motel in Hot Springs. As his mother left the room, Ray stared at his poster.

"Should we tell her?" asked Liz.

"No way," said Ray. "Who would ever believe a crazy story like that?"

Identify Setting

In a time-travel story, the setting is very important. Go back through the story. The setting changes a few times. Find each change. Then fill in the chart below. Describe where and when each part of the story happens. The last setting is almost the same as one of the other settings.

Beginning [Setting 1]

Where?: **Museum in Hot Springs, SD**

When?: **Present time**

What happened?: _____

Middle [Setting 2]

Where?: _____

When?: _____

What happened?: _____

End [Setting 3]

Where?: _____

When?: _____

What happened?: _____

Summarize

Finish each sentence below to create a summary of the story. Use the chart on page 107 to help you.

The title of the story is _____.

The main characters are _____ and _____.

At first, we meet them in _____.

Suddenly, they are in a _____.

They see a _____ and a _____.

Finally, they are in a _____ with their mother.

Identify Details

Read the five sentences below. Decide which are the two most important details about the story. Fill in the two bubbles. Check to see if you included the details in your summary.

Ⓐ Ray is Liz's brother.

Ⓑ Ray and Liz were visiting a museum in Hot Springs, South Dakota, to see mammoth bones.

Ⓒ Ray and Liz were with their mother.

Ⓓ Ray knew that mammoths were not meat eaters.

Ⓔ Ray and Liz traveled back to the time of the mammoths.

Frozen in Time

In many countries in the world, scientists have found parts of woolly mammoths. These creatures had been in the ground for thousands of years. What can scientists learn from these amazing finds?

Think About Genre

Look at the pages of this **nonfiction article**. Then read each statement below. Put an **X** next to each statement that you think describes this article.

_____ It gives information.

_____ It is a fantasy story.

_____ It is mostly about people who lived long ago.

_____ It tells about things that really happened.

Think About the Topic

Read the introduction to "Frozen in Time" again. Ask yourself: *What do I already know about mammoths?* Write two things you know on the lines below.

1. _____

   _____

2. _____

   _____

Preview and Predict

Take a quick look at the article. Then predict what you will learn when you read "Frozen in Time."

_____

_____

Early humans used mammoth bones and furs to make shelters.

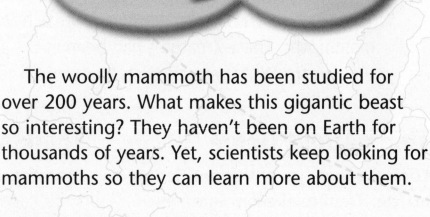

Frozen in Time

STRATEGIES

MAKE INFERENCES
UNDERSTAND GENRE
MAKE CONNECTIONS

MAKE INFERENCES

Use the clues an author gives you and what you already know to figure things out.

Why is it rare to find the whole body of a mammoth?

_____

_____

_____

_____

_____

The woolly mammoth has been studied for over 200 years. What makes this gigantic beast so interesting? They haven't been on Earth for thousands of years. Yet, scientists keep looking for mammoths so they can learn more about them.

What's Been Found

Scientists were excited to find the first, frozen body of a mammoth several years ago. This mammoth still had **flesh** and hair. Ice **preserved** the body in one piece after the mammoth died over 23,000 years ago. In 2006, the complete skeleton of a mammoth was found. This is also very rare.

Most of the time, scientists have only parts of a mammoth to study. Scientists still learn a lot about mammoths from parts like bones, hair, teeth, tusks, and pieces of skin or flesh.

flesh (FLESH) the soft part of the body that covers the bones
preserved (prih-ZURVD) kept from rotting or spoiling

A scientist examines 23,000-year-old mammoth teeth

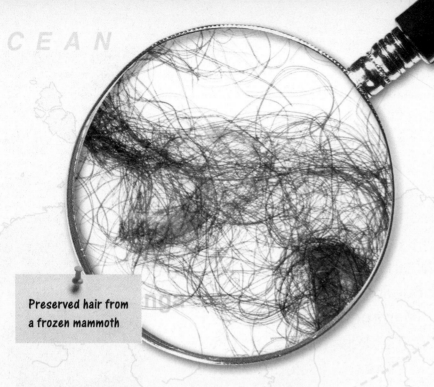

Preserved hair from
a frozen mammoth

Mammoth Discovery Sites

Woolly mammoth remains have been found in North America, Africa, Europe, and Asia. In North America, people can visit a museum in Hot Springs, South Dakota, to see hundreds of mammoth remains. The museum was built around the **site** where they were found. In Europe, mammoth remains have been found in countries such as England, Spain, and Germany. Some of the most famous mammoths found in Asia were preserved in ice in Siberia. Siberia is the area that covers most of northern Asia. These mammoth bodies or skeletons were found whole. Others have been found in African countries, where the mammoths are believed to have come from.

What They've Learned

Mammoths weren't as large as most people think they are. They were just a bit taller than modern-day elephants. Scientists found mammoths that were 11 to 13 feet tall at the shoulder and weighed about six to eight **tons**.

UNDERSTAND GENRE
(article)
Real places are often included in articles. Write the name of one place that is included. Explain why it is important to include it in the article.

_____

_____

_____

_____

_____

_____

site (SITE) a place where something is found

ton (TUHN) a unit of weight that equals 2,000 pounds

determine (dih-TUR-min)
to discover or figure out

paleontologists (pay-lee-on-TOL-uh-jists)
scientists who study living things that lived thousands of years ago

Compared to elephants, a mammoth's tusks were a lot longer and more curved. However, the mammoth's ears were a lot smaller than the ears of elephants. Mammoth ears were only about one foot long. An African elephant has ears that are about six feet long.

Mammoths had long, thick hair that kept them warm in cold climates. In 2006, scientists learned through lab studies that the coat colors of mammoths were either dark brown or blonde.

Scientists have also found and looked at the stomach of a frozen mammoth. More than 30 pounds of grass and other plants were still inside! Their teeth were made for chewing the rough greens. Scientists know that mammoths lost teeth and grew new ones about six times in their lifetime. As the mammoths got older, their teeth got bigger. Scientists have used the teeth that were found to **determine** how old a mammoth was when it died.

No one really knows why mammoths disappeared. Some scientists think it has to do with changes in climate. Others think that humans hunted them until there were none left. Some other scientists believe that maybe a disease killed the mammoths.

Paleontologists will continue to uncover and study mammoths. Someday, they may know for sure why mammoths no longer live on Earth.

Model of a full-sized mammoth

Identify Details

"Frozen in Time" has three sections. Each section has a heading. It tells what the section is about. Read the heading below. Then reread the section. Write four important details from that section.

What They've Learned

Detail 1: _____

_____

Detail 2: _____

_____

Detail 3: _____

_____

Detail 4: _____

_____

Summarize

To write a summary of "Frozen in Time," you should include the most important details from each section. Review each section of the article. Then write your summary below.

_____

_____

_____

_____

_____

_____

Mammoth tusks could be as long as 17 feet.

Identify Details

You can often find important facts by asking _What? Where? Who? When?_ or _Why?_

Write an important fact from the article that answers some questions below.

What have scientists studied? _____

Where have mammoths been found? _____

Why are mammoths studied?_____

_____

Make Connections

Think about "A Mammoth Adventure" and "Frozen in Time." Answer the questions to connect the selections to each other and to you.

1. What is one detail you learned about woolly mammoths from the story that is also true in the article?

_____

_____

_____

2. What might life be like for people and mammoths if mammoths were alive today? Use what you learned about mammoths to write your answer.

_____

_____

_____

3. Think about what you have read in both selections. Would you like to study mammoths? Tell why or why not.

_____

_____

_____

Write an Invitation

What if you really could travel back in time? Write an invitation to a friend or relative. Write where you would be going and when you would be leaving. Give reasons why you think it would be a great trip.

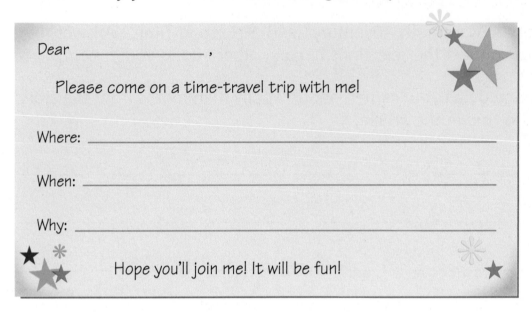

Dear _____ ,

Please come on a time-travel trip with me!

Where: _____

When: _____

Why: _____

Hope you'll join me! It will be fun!

 Before you write, use the *You're Invited* handout your teacher will give you to plan your invitation.

Plan Your Research

What else would you like to learn about mammoths or other Ice Age animals? Write two questions that you would like to have answered.

1. _____

_____

2. _____

_____

How could a rabbit and a coyote help people?
Find out in these two myths. They were told by
the Paiute (PIE-yoot) Indians of the American West.

Think About Genre

Myths are stories that people have told for many years. No one knows who first told the story. People passed myths on from one storyteller to the next. Hundreds of years passed before the stories were written.

Myths are made-up stories that tell about things in nature. Myths may explain how things first began.

Fill in the bubble next to two statements that describe a myth.

(A) It tells of a time long ago.

(B) Only real people are in the story.

(C) It explains something in nature and how it first began.

(D) It has only facts you can check.

Think About the Topic

Think about the titles "Sunlight" and "Fire." Ask yourself: *Why are sunlight and fire important?* Complete each sentence.

Sunlight is important because

_____ .

Fire is important because

_____ .

Preview and Predict

Reread the introduction and take a look at the stories. What do you think rabbit and coyote will do?

Rabbit: _____

_____

Coyote: _____

_____

STRATEGIES

MAKE INFERENCES
MAKE CONNECTIONS
UNDERSTAND GENRE

Sunlight and Fire

MAKE INFERENCES
Use details in a story and what you know to help you figure out something.

I know the sun rises in the east, so that's why the author has Tavu travel east.

Think about Tavu's tears. Why did they keep the arrows from burning up?

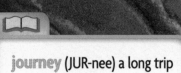

journey (JUR-nee) a long trip
weep (WEEP) to cry

Sunlight

A long time ago, there were not many hours of daylight. Days were very short. The Paiute people did not have enough time to hunt. The rabbit Tavu wanted to help, so he decided to go to the place where daylight began. He packed up his arrows and set out on a journey east toward the sun.

Tavu traveled far. At last he came to the edge of the world, where the sun lived. He hid behind some rocks and waited for the sun to come out.

As soon as the sun began to rise, Tavu raised his arrow, took aim, and shot it. The arrow quickly burned up before it reached the sun. Tavu tried again. He walked closer to the sun, shooting arrows as he went. Every arrow burst into flames before it reached its mark.

Finally, there were only two arrows left. Tavu began to weep. He cried so much that his tears caused his last two arrows to become soaking wet. He took aim again and shot the first of those two arrows. Tavu smiled. It almost hit the sun!

Then Tavu let his last arrow fly. This time, the arrow hit! The sun fell to the ground.

Quickly, Tavu cut the sun into pieces. He threw one piece into the sky.

"Go higher and make the days longer," he commanded. Then he ran away as fast as he could.

Every time the angry sun tried to chase Tavu, Tavu hid. At last the sun gave up. Tavu watched it move higher and higher into the sky. He was very pleased. "Now the day will be long enough," he said.

When Tavu returned, the people celebrated. They held a big sun dance. Then they asked Tavu to do even more.

"Go fight the sun again," they begged. "We want daylight all the time."

"No," said Tavu. "You need night as well as day. You need time for sleeping."

And from that day to this, there has been daylight and night.

Fire

A long time ago, the Paiute people had no fire. They were cold and miserable all winter long. Finally, a boy decided to do something about it. He went to Coyote to ask for his help.

MAKE CONNECTIONS
When reading a story, compare it to what you already know.

How do you explain daylight and night?

celebrated (SEL-uh-brayt-id) honored with a party

commanded (kuh-MAND-id) gave an order

miserable (MIZ-ur-uh-buhl) very unhappy or sad

UNDERSTAND GENRE
(myth)
In Native American myths, animals often help people. The Paiute told myths about how the rabbit and the coyote helped them.

Write two examples that tell you this story is made up.

_____

_____

_____

_____

_____

Coyote knew where to get fire. "We must go west to the Burning Mountain," he said. "But," he warned, "it is very dangerous. We will need many fast runners."

The boy told his people. Soon all the best runners were ready. Coyote led the way.

They walked for many days. Every night, they stopped to leave one runner behind. There the runner would wait.

Soon, only the boy and Coyote were left. And then even Coyote was on his own. He crept slowly up to the place where the Fire Beings lived. He waited patiently for the chance to take a blazing piece of wood. It did not take long. He grabbed the wood and ran as fast as he could. The angry Fire Beings chased him to where he was going. The boy stood waiting below.

Coyote passed the burning wood to the boy. The boy ran until he came to the next runner, who took the wood and ran to the next. In this way, the fire passed from runner to runner. The Fire Beings could not catch up to the runners.

Now the people had fire for cooking and heat. From then on, Coyote was called the Fire Bringer.

blazing (BLAZ-ing) burning or on fire
crept (KREPT) moved slowly in a sneaky way
dangerous (DAYN-jur-us) unsafe

UNDERSTANDING FICTION

Compare and Contrast

The two myths you have read are alike in many ways. Use the chart below to help you compare them. Read the questions. Then review each myth. Write your answers in the chart.

"Sunlight" and "Fire": Two Paiute Myths

	Sunlight	Fire
1. When does the story take place?		
2. What problem did the people have?		
3. What animal helped them?		
4. How did the animal help?		
5. What changed for the people?		

Summarize

A good way to summarize these two myths is to tell briefly how they are alike. Use the information in your chart on page 121 to help you.

_____

_____

_____

_____

_____

_____

Identify Details

To remember these myths, you should recall the most important details. Read each pair of sentences below. Fill in the bubble beside the sentence that is most important for retelling the myths.

1. Ⓐ Tavu shot the sun with an arrow.
   Ⓑ Tavu's friends held a dance.

2. Ⓐ Coyote helped people get fire.
   Ⓑ Coyote passed the fire to a boy.

3. Ⓐ Burning Mountain was in the West.
   Ⓑ The people had no fire.

Sarah Winnemucca

In the 1800s, the Paiute people needed a real-life hero. Sarah Winnemucca (wihn-uh-MUHK-uh), the daughter of a Paiute leader, had a special skill with words. Could she, like Tavu and Coyote, help her people?

Think About Genre

The two myths you read told about brave animals who helped the Paiute people. Next, you will read a **biography** about a real Paiute woman. You've read biographies of George Washington and Zora Neale Hurston. Tell what a biography is.

_____

_____

_____

_____

Think About the Topic

Reread the introduction to "Sarah Winnemucca." Ask yourself: *What does it tell me about her?* Write three ideas on the lines below.

1. _____

2. _____

3. _____

Preview and Predict

Preview the biography. Write one idea you think you will learn.

_____

_____

_____

The pinyon pine cone produces pine nuts. They were very valuable to the Paiute diet.

STRATEGIES

**MAKE INFERENCES
MAKE CONNECTIONS
UNDERSTAND GENRE**

Sarah Winnemucca

MAKE INFERENCES

Use details from the biography and what you know to figure out something.

> I wonder why there were fewer animals to hunt. I guess the strangers did a lot of hunting, too.

Why did Truckee believe that the Paiute could survive if they lived with the strangers?

_____

_____

_____

Sarah Winnemucca was a northern Paiute Indian. She was born in 1844 in what is now the state of Nevada. Her Paiute name was Thocmetony (THOCK-muh-toe-ne), which means "shell flower."

When Thocmetony was small, her family moved from place to place to find food. They fished and hunted. They gathered pine nuts. Food was scarce in their land, but they had enough to eat.

Soon the Paiute way of life began to change. Strangers came into Paiute land. They brought cattle with them. They cut down trees. Now there were fewer pine nuts to gather. There were fewer animals to hunt. Life became difficult.

Many Paiutes wanted to fight. They wanted to drive the strangers out of their land. Thocmetony's grandfather, Truckee, (TRUHK-ee) had a different idea. He believed that these strangers were brothers to the Paiute.

He believed that the only way the Paiute could survive was to learn to live together.

scarce (SKAIRS) hard to get; not much

survive (sur-VIVE) to go on being; to stay alive

Time Line of Sarah Winnemucca's Life

Makes first trip to California	Goes to girls' school in California for 3 weeks	Becomes an interpreter
Born		
1840	1850	1860

Nevada Valley

Thocmetony was afraid of the white strangers. In 1850, when she was six, Truckee decided to take her to California. He wanted her to meet these people and see how they lived. In California, she met many good people. She learned to be less afraid.

Truckee wanted his grandchildren to learn the ways of other people. Thocmetony began to learn English. She was given the name Sarah.

When Sarah was 13, she and her sister, Elma, went to live with a white family in Nevada. They learned to speak and write in English. Sarah was a quick learner. She had a special gift for language.

Meanwhile, life for the Paiute became worse. More and more strangers came. They took away Paiute land and food. Sometimes they killed Paiute people for no reason.

Sarah knew she must do something. She began to fight for her people with the only weapon she had. She began to use her skill with words.

MAKE CONNECTIONS

To understand a biography, think about how you would feel if you were that person.

Tell about a time you felt less scared after getting to know someone or something.

_____

_____

_____

_____

_____

_____

weapon (WEP-un)
something used in fighting

Timeline:

1870	1880	1890	1900
Goes to Washington, D.C.	Marries Lewis H. Hopkins	Publishes her book, *Life Among the Piutes*	Starts a school
			Dies

UNDERSTAND GENRE
(biography)

A person's life has many events. An author has to choose just a few of those events for a short biography such as this one. Write down one event in Sarah Winnemucca's life. Tell why you think the author decided to include it.

_____

_____

_____

_____

_____

_____

beliefs (bee-LEEFS) a feeling that something is real

interpreter (in-TER-pruh-ter) a person who explains what words mean from one language to another

At the time, people in the United States knew that there were problems between Native Americans and others. Most people had heard only one side of the story. Sarah wanted them to learn the Native American side, too.

Sarah worked as an **interpreter**. She wrote letters in English to important people. She explained Paiute **beliefs** in English so others could understand their way of life. Sarah discovered that people listened to her when she wore her native costume. They would come to the theater to see her up on the stage sharing stories about the Paiute.

In 1880, Sarah went to Washington, D.C., to meet with the president of the United States. In 1883, she wrote a book about her people and their ways. It was the first book written by a Native American woman.

Sarah had many hopes for her people. The work she did was very important. She helped to build a bridge of understanding between two very different ways of life.

Sarah, dressed in her native costume

Identify Details

The author tells about Sarah Winnemucca's life through three main ideas. Other details in the biography give more information about those main ideas.

Read each main idea in the chart below. Then read through the biography to find two details that tell about each main idea. Write one detail in each box under the main idea. Write the page you found it on.

Main Idea: The Paiute way of life changed when strangers came into their land.	Main Idea: Sarah learned the language and ways of strangers.	Main Idea: Sarah used words to help people understand each other.
Detail: _____ _____ _____ Page: _____	Detail: _____ _____ _____ Page: _____	Detail: _____ _____ _____ Page: _____
Detail: _____ _____ _____ Page: _____	Detail: _____ _____ _____ Page: _____	Detail: _____ _____ _____ Page: _____

Summarize

One way to summarize a biography is by answering the questions *Who? When? Where? What? Why?* and *How?* Answer these questions about "Sarah Winnemucca."

Who was Sarah Winnemucca? _____

When did she live? _____

Where did she live? _____

What was happening at that time? _____

_____

Why did Sarah move to California and Nevada? _____

_____

How did she "build a bridge of understanding"? _____

_____

Identify Details

If you were to retell Sarah Winnemucca's biography, you would tell only the most important events. Which details below are important enough to be included in a brief summary? Fill in the bubble next to three of the most important sentences.

(A) Sarah's Paiute name, Thocmetony, is the name of a flower.

(B) Sarah was very skillful in using the English language.

(C) The Paiute ate pine nuts.

(D) Sarah's grandfather took her to California.

(E) Sarah wrote a book to tell others about Paiute life.

The book Sarah Winnemucca Hopkins wrote: *Life Among the Piutes—Their Wrongs and Claims*

Make Connections

Think about how the two selections you have read connect to each other and to you. Answer the following questions.

1. What is one detail you learned about the Paiute from each selection?

1. _____

_____

2. _____

_____

2. What is one way Sarah Winnemucca is like Tavu and Coyote?

_____

_____

3. The Paiute often used myths to explain how things in nature come to be. What sources would you use to learn about nature? How are those sources different than myths?

_____

_____

_____

_____

Write a Myth

Think about the two Paiute myths you have read. Use the space below to make some notes for a myth about nature. Write your myth on a separate sheet of paper.

_____

_____

_____

_____

_____

Before you write, use the *Nature Myth* handout your teacher will give you to plan your myth.

Native American headdress used during ceremonies

Plan Your Research

What else would you like to know about Sarah Winnemucca? Write two questions on the lines below.

1. _____

_____

2. _____

_____

This part of the lesson is a test. After you read "Tiger Gets His Stripes," you will be asked questions about the selection. These questions will test how well you understand the reading strategies you have practiced.

Tiger wishes he were like a leopard so he could be a better hunter. Then he'd have spots, and he'd be able to climb trees. Will anything make Tiger change the way he feels?

Think About Genre

The story you will read is a **fantasy**. This kind of **fiction** includes events that cannot happen in real life. In a fantasy story, animals may talk, or they may behave like people.

Read each of the following sentences. Put an **X** beside the two sentences that describe something that could happen only in a fantasy.

☐ A cat talks on a phone.

☐ A boy goes to the zoo.

☐ A girl takes a trip in a time machine.

☐ A person makes a friend.

Think About the Topic

Read the introduction to "Tiger Gets His Stripes" again. Ask yourself: *What do I know about tigers in real life?* Write one thing you know about tigers.

_____

_____

Preview and Predict

Look ahead at the story's pictures. What do you think will happen to the tiger in the story?

_____

_____

TIGER
Gets His Stripes

At sunrise, Tiger **sauntered** across the forest. Once again, Tiger had not caught any prey during the night. He had come close, but a speedy antelope had outrun Tiger. A rabbit had climbed up a tree. Then a deer had seen Tiger watching him and dashed off. They were all so good at escaping Tiger!

Tiger was big, strong, and scary-looking. But he wasn't sneaky like the smaller animals. They always noticed him so easily!

Tiger wished he could be more like the spotted leopard. Leopard could climb trees and hide in them. Leopard's spots blended in with the leaves and the bark.

"If I only had some spots and knew how to climb trees," Tiger whispered as he stretched out in the grass to sleep. "I could hide and sneak up on the other animals. Life would be great!"

Just then a beautiful, striped butterfly rose out of the tall grass. She fluttered above him.

"Was that you I heard whispering?" Butterfly said, in her smooth voice.

sauntered (SAWN-terd)
walked slowly

"Um, yes, but I was talking to myself, miss," responded Tiger.

"You know, I didn't like being stuck in my cocoon," said Butterfly, "I wanted to be anything but a cooped-up insect."

"But you grew wings. Now you can fly," said Tiger.

"That's my point. Later on I wasn't sorry to be me." With that, Butterfly flew away into the trees.

Tiger didn't understand. It was great that she could fly. But he couldn't climb trees, and he couldn't hide from anybody.

As Tiger walked away, he heard a cat cry out in the woods. Who was it? He headed into the forest to find out.

He quickly spotted the cause of the loud cry. A leopard lay on the forest floor. Leopard's paw was trapped under a big, heavy tree branch.

"Oh, please help me, Tiger!" said Leopard.

"What happened?" asked Tiger, as he walked closer.

"I was sleeping up in the branches. All at once, the branch snapped, and I fell with it. Now I'm trapped under it!"

"Let's see if I can help," said Tiger, suddenly glad he couldn't climb trees.

Tiger wedged his body under the tree. He pushed and he pushed.

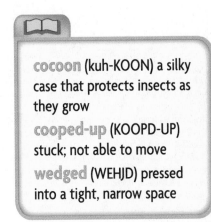

cocoon (kuh-KOON) a silky case that protects insects as they grow

cooped-up (KOOPD-UP) stuck; not able to move

wedged (WEHJD) pressed into a tight, narrow space

Leopard said, "If anyone can help me, it's you."

With a final push, Tiger rolled the branch off of Leopard's paw.

"You're lucky to be so strong!" cried Leopard. "What would I have done without you?"

"It's nothing, Leopard," called Tiger, suddenly glad of his own strength and size.

Then Tiger noticed Butterfly watching him in the distance. What was she doing?

Butterfly flew to Tiger. "Ah, Tiger," she said, smiling. "You have done well. Do you still feel the same way about being a tiger?"

Tiger thought and said, "No. I'm glad to be a tiger."

Butterfly said, "You have become proud of who you are. That is a powerful thing. You have earned a special gift. I will give you stripes to help you hide. But you must wear your stripes with pride. They are yours, and only yours, forever."

Butterfly landed on Tiger's back and flapped her wings three times. All at once, he had stripes all over his fur. The black and orange pattern dazzled him!

"Thank you, Butterfly!" cried Tiger.

But Butterfly had already fluttered away. Over her wings, she called "Off to Africa! Some zebras need my help!"

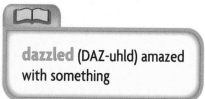

dazzled (DAZ-uhld) amazed with something

Use what you have read to answer questions 1–7.

Multiple Choice

1. Which of the following events happens first in the story?

    Ⓐ Butterfly gives Tiger his stripes.

    Ⓑ Leopard's paw is trapped under a branch.

    Ⓒ Tiger wishes he were more like a leopard.

    Ⓓ Butterfly says she didn't like being in a cocoon.

2. Which detail makes the story a fantasy?

    Ⓐ Tiger talks to Leopard and Butterfly.

    Ⓑ Leopard sleeps in a tree.

    Ⓒ Tiger and Leopard live in a forest.

    Ⓓ Tiger goes hunting for food.

3. How do you think Butterfly might help the zebras?

    Ⓐ She will teach them how to cook.

    Ⓑ She will teach them how to read books about butterflies.

    Ⓒ She will play a game with them.

    Ⓓ She will teach them about their stripes.

4. Why does Tiger become happy about being a tiger?

    Ⓐ Tiger thinks flying is too hard.

    Ⓑ Tiger is glad that he can now live in a cocoon.

    Ⓒ Tiger is glad he was strong enough to help Leopard.

    Ⓓ Tiger doesn't think stripes look good on him.

5. What detail helps you **best** see that Tiger works hard to move the fallen tree?

   (A) Tiger has to push more than once.

   (B) Leopard's paw was trapped.

   (C) Butterfly is watching.

   (D) Tiger becomes glad that he can't climb trees.

6. Why does Leopard tell Tiger, "If anyone can help me, it's you"?

   (A) Leopard thinks Tiger is smarter than Butterfly.

   (B) Tiger is bigger and stronger than other animals.

   (C) Leopard knows that tigers cannot climb trees.

   (D) Tiger is the only other animal in the forest.

Short Response

7. How did Butterfly help Tiger be proud of who he is? Use details from the story to help you write your answer.

_____

_____

_____

_____

_____

_____

 This is the end of the test for "Tiger Gets His Stripes." When your teacher tells you, go on to read the next selection, "Cats in the Wild."

CATS in the Wild

This part of the lesson is a test. After you read "Cats in the Wild," you will be asked questions about the selection. These questions will test your understanding of the strategies you have practiced.

Unlike pets, leopard and tigers live on their own in the wild. Do you know the difference between a leopard and a tiger? Read on to learn more about these wild cats.

Think About Genre

Nonfiction articles give true information. They have many features that help readers. Look through "Cats in the Wild." Put an **X** next to each thing you see.

☐ photographs

☐ captions that explain photos

☐ headings that tell about each part

Think About the Topic

Reread the introduction. Think about what you know about tigers and leopards. Write one thing you know about each animal.

Tigers: _____

_____

Leopards: _____

_____

Preview and Predict

Read the headings and look at the photos in "Cats in the Wild" again. Predict one thing you might learn from the article.

_____

_____

This leopard's spots, called rosettes, help protect it from predators.

© Options Publishing. No copying permitted.

CATS in the Wild

Did you know that there are over forty different types of cats in the world? Some weigh just a few pounds. The largest cats can be as big as a small car! Leopards and tigers are two types of cats that live in the wild.

How to "Spot" a Leopard

Leopards are found on two continents, Asia and Africa. The male leopards are larger than the females. Leopards may weigh up to 200 pounds and be six feet long. In the wild, they live for about 15 years. In zoos, leopards may live longer because there they are protected from predators. Leopards can be found in many different habitats. They live in mountains, forests, deserts, and grassy areas. In sunnier, grassy areas, their fur may look lighter. In dark, dense forests, their fur may look almost black. These differences help leopards blend in with the woods.

habitats (HAB-ih-tats) areas where animals or plants can be found

predators (PRED-uh-turz) animals that hunt other animals

This leopard lives in a dense forest. It has darker fur.

The spots on a leopard's fur help it blend in with the woods. Because leopards are not a solid color, they can be harder to see. Their spotted fur helps leopards sneak up on their prey and helps protect them from predators.

Leopards often sleep or rest during the day. They like to climb trees and sprawl out on high limbs. They also enjoy swimming. At night, they hunt for food. Leopards are carnivores, so they hunt other animals. They use their eyes and ears to find prey, such as monkeys, birds, and antelopes. But leopards sometimes hunt animals bigger than themselves!

Tiger Time

Tigers are the largest cats in the world. They can grow to be 10 feet long. That's as long as a small car! Tigers can weigh over 500 pounds. Like leopards, tigers live for about 15 years in the wild. Tigers are only found in forests in Asia.

Most cats like to live alone. Tigers, however, can be social. They sometimes live together. Even if they live alone, tigers use their sense of smell to keep track of other tigers that live in their area.

The Siberian, or Amur, tiger is the largest kind of tiger.

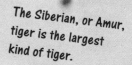

carnivores (CAHR-nuh-vorz) animals that eat only meat

social (SOSH-ul) likes to be around other people or animals

Tigers are also carnivores. They hunt mostly at night. Their prey includes wild boar, deer, and wild cattle.

Tigers are well known for their stripes, which help them blend in with the grasses around them. Their camouflage helps them hunt prey and hide from predators. Did you know that every tiger has a different pattern of stripes, much like each person has different fingerprints?

Tigers are strong swimmers. They enjoy the water. In this way, they are like leopards. But unlike leopards, tigers can't climb trees as well.

Cats in Trouble

Today, there are eight kinds of leopards and six kinds of tigers living in the world. They are all endangered. Their habitats are disappearing. People cut down trees and build on their land. Some people kill them for their fur or to keep them from hunting farm animals.

Many people are helping leopards and tigers. They are trying to protect them and save their homes. Laws have been passed so people cannot kill them. If people work together, these wild cats can be saved.

camouflage
(CAM-uh-flazh) the hiding of something; a disguise
endangered
(en-DANE-jurd) at risk for dying out

The South Chinese tiger is the most endangered kind of tiger.

Use what you have read to answer questions 1–7.

Multiple Choice

1. Which detail helps you **best** visualize how long a tiger can grow to be?

   Ⓐ Tigers can weigh over 500 pounds.

   Ⓑ Tigers can be the size of a small car.

   Ⓒ Tigers are also carnivores.

   Ⓓ Tigers enjoy swimming.

2. Which statement **best** describes the main idea of "Cats in the Wild"?

   Ⓐ Wild cats come in many shapes and sizes.

   Ⓑ Leopards and tigers need land.

   Ⓒ Leopards and tigers can be compared in many ways.

   Ⓓ Leopards and tigers are wild cats that have fur.

3. What might happen if people stop taking the land of leopards and tigers?

   Ⓐ Leopards and tigers will all die.

   Ⓑ Leopards and tigers will keep living.

   Ⓒ Leopards and tigers will have no place to live.

   Ⓓ Leopards and tigers will have no food.

4. Which detail explains why tigers probably don't sleep in trees?

   Ⓐ Tigers are not good climbers.

   Ⓑ Tigers are not good swimmers.

   Ⓒ Tigers are endangered.

   Ⓓ Tigers do not have stripes.

© Options Publishing. No copying permitted.

5. Why do leopards and tigers **most** likely hunt at night?

Ⓐ Leopards and tigers like to sleep late during the day.

Ⓑ Leopards and tigers can't see during the day.

Ⓒ Leopards and tigers like to swim at night.

Ⓓ Leopards and tigers can better sneak up on prey when it is dark.

6. You can tell that "Cats in the Wild" is a nonfiction article because

Ⓐ it tells about things that wild cats can't do in real life.

Ⓑ it takes place in the future.

Ⓒ it has true information about wild cats.

Ⓓ it tells about two wild cats that are made-up characters.

Short Response

7. Describe three ways that leopards and tigers are alike. Use details from the article to write your answer.

_____

_____

_____

_____

_____

_____

 STOP **This is the end of the test for "Cats in the Wild."**
When your teacher tells you, continue on and finish the last part of the test.

Use what you have read in both selections to answer questions 1–5.

Multiple Choice

1. What does Tiger do in "Tiger Gets His Stripes" that real tigers do in "Cats in the Wild"?

   Ⓐ Tiger wishes for spotted fur.

   Ⓑ Tiger keeps track of other tigers.

   Ⓒ Tiger hunts at night and relaxes during the day.

   Ⓓ Tiger goes swimming.

2. In which part of the world could Tiger and Leopard live near each other?

   Ⓐ Asia

   Ⓑ Africa

   Ⓒ North America

   Ⓓ Australia

3. What is one way Leopard might tell Tiger apart from other tigers?

   Ⓐ Tiger has spots instead of stripes.

   Ⓑ Tiger's stripes are different from every other tiger's stripes.

   Ⓒ Tiger is the smallest tiger in the world.

   Ⓓ Tiger likes to climb trees.

4. Think about what you learned about tigers in the article. Explain two other things about tigers that would make Tiger in the story feel proud.

   _____

   _____

   _____

   _____

   _____

5. Write a letter that tells a friend what you have learned about real leopards and tigers. Be sure to include a greeting and a closing in your letter.

_____

_____

_____

_____

_____

_____

_____

_____

_____

_____

_____

_____

STOP **This is the end of the test.**

Best Practices in Reading

Practice Test 1

Student's Name _____ Grade _____

School Name _____

Teacher's Name _____

Test	Items	Possible Score	Student Score
Vocabulary in Context	1–15	15	
Reading Comprehension	16–35	20	
Total	35	35	

I. Vocabulary
Fill in the letter of the word that best fits in the sentence.

1. The crew worked hard to _____ the man who was trapped under the ice.
   - (A) rescue
   - (B) jungle
   - (C) problem
   - (D) invent

2. Jenna put three slices of _____ on her sandwich.
   - (A) chatter
   - (B) feast
   - (C) thick
   - (D) tomato

3. Many people who have come to America to start a new life have had to _____ to get by.
   - (A) drawer
   - (B) ruin
   - (C) rule
   - (D) struggle

4. His homework was in his bag last night, but what happened to it since is _____.
   - (A) a mystery
   - (B) a choice
   - (C) able
   - (D) an answer

5. James wrote ideas for his next story in his _____.
   - (A) life
   - (B) camera
   - (C) notebook
   - (D) upset

6. Kuan-yin read books about space because she wanted to be a _____ astronaut.
   - (A) famous
   - (B) past
   - (C) worse
   - (D) lazy

7. His family was very _____ when he told them he won first prize.
   - (A) leftover
   - (B) proud
   - (C) easier
   - (D) disturbed

8. With supplies and a map, they set out to _____ the island.
   - (A) dinner
   - (B) faraway
   - (C) explore
   - (D) balance

9. Many times the _____ in folktales are animals.
   - (A) characters
   - (B) grocery
   - (C) myths
   - (D) museum

10. Could you do me a _____ and help me move this box to the attic?
    - (A) handle
    - (B) package
    - (C) favor
    - (D) thankful

11. The flowers on this plant _____ from one to three inches wide.
    - (A) range
    - (B) waxy
    - (C) along
    - (D) wonder

12. The people without umbrellas were _____ during the heavy rain.
    - (A) glider
    - (B) comfortable
    - (C) melting
    - (D) miserable

13. The tourists stopped at an inn during their _____.

   Ⓐ conductor   Ⓒ journey

   Ⓑ beginning   Ⓓ distance

14. The Patriots decided to _____ an army against Britain.

   Ⓐ trade   Ⓒ vote

   Ⓑ buzz   Ⓓ form

15. Scientists _____ the bones that were frozen in ice.

   Ⓐ decorated   Ⓒ examined

   Ⓑ caused   Ⓓ knelt

II. Reading Comprehension
Read each passage. Answer the questions that follow.

It Is Grand

Jared looked across the front seat at his father. His father was humming. "Just a few more miles, Jared," Dad said, "and we will see one of the wonders of the world!"

Driving across the country to see the Grand Canyon was not how Jared wanted to spend the summer. Right now his friends were probably diving into the new city pool. Jared had been looking forward to the new pool all year. He thought back to April, when his dad first told him about the plans he had made for the two of them to drive from Boston to Arizona. He remembered how he started to complain. Then his father began telling him about how he had been saving money and time off from work for this trip. Jared told his friends to have fun without him.

Jared and his father had been driving for over a week. They had been to an amusement park in Pennsylvania. They had visited his aunt in St. Louis. They had slept in a tent in Oklahoma. But most of the time they spent in the car, driving miles and miles west each day.

"Son, this is what we have been waiting for," Jared's dad said suddenly. Jared stared ahead at the huge hole in the earth. He didn't know that the color brown came in so many shades or that it could be so beautiful. The sky was a perfect blue. It was full of puffy clouds that made shadows on the cliffs below. Jared felt so small. But for the first time in his life, he didn't mind feeling small. The world really was wonderful. "Dad," Jared began when he caught his breath, "it was worth every second it took to get here."

16. This passage is mostly about—

Ⓐ things to do in the Grand Canyon.

Ⓑ the land and rivers in the west.

Ⓒ a father and son's trip.

Ⓓ ways to travel across country.

17. How did Jared's dad feel about the trip?

Ⓐ excited   Ⓒ sad

Ⓑ bored   Ⓓ nervous

18. What will Jared probably tell his friends when he gets home?

Ⓐ I wish I had been in the pool instead.

Ⓑ My father didn't even want to go.

Ⓒ It doesn't take that long to go from Boston to Arizona.

Ⓓ The Grand Canyon is beautiful.

19. Which best tells what kind of text this passage is?

Ⓐ It is a story that could be real.

Ⓑ It is a fantasy that could not really happen.

Ⓒ It is a mystery.

Ⓓ It is a nonfiction science article.

Write your answer on the lines below.

20. What changed Jared's mind about the trip?

_____

_____

The Natural Wonders of the World

You might have heard about the Seven Wonders of the World. They were built by people long ago, although people today aren't sure how. There are also Wonders of the natural world. These are places on Earth that were made by nature, not people.

The Natural Wonders of the World are spread around the earth. There are two in Africa, three in Asia, one in Australia, four in North America, and two in South America.

Four of the Natural Wonders of the World are waterfalls. They are Angel Falls in Venezuela, Iguassu Falls in Brazil and Argentina, Niagara Falls in Canada and the United States, and Victoria Falls in Zambia and Zimbabwe. Angel Falls is the largest waterfall in the world. It is 3,212 feet high and 500 feet wide. At these waterfalls, a great amount of water flows quickly over high rocks and crashes far below.

Three of the Natural Wonders are mountains. They are Mount Everest in Nepal, Mount Fuji in Japan, and Mount Kilimanjaro in Tanzania. Mount Everest is the highest point on Earth. It is 29,028 feet tall. That is almost five miles high or almost as tall as 20 Empire State Buildings stacked on top of each other!

Two of the Natural Wonders of the World are volcanoes. A volcano is a hole in the earth that sometimes lets out hot rock and ash. Often a mountain or hill forms around the hole when the rock and ash cool. Krakatoa Island in Indonesia and Paracutin Volcano in Mexico are both Natural Wonders.

The other Natural Wonders of the World are much different. The Bay of Fundy in Canada has the highest and strongest tides in the world. It is home to more whales than anywhere else. The Great Barrier Reef off the coast of Australia is another Natural Wonder that is home to many animals. The Great Barrier Reef is made of the skeletons of tiny sea creatures that have built up over millions of years. It is more than 1,250 miles long. The last Natural Wonder of the World is the Grand Canyon in the United States. The Grand Canyon is a long, narrow valley in Arizona that was formed by water cutting through the ground. Many people travel to the Grand Canyon every year to see interesting shapes of rocks and beautiful colors.

GO ON

21. Which is the <u>most important</u> idea of the article?

    Ⓐ Mount Everest is 29,028 feet tall.

    Ⓑ There are four Natural Wonders in North America.

    Ⓒ The Natural Wonders were made by nature.

    Ⓓ Many people travel to the Grand Canyon every year.

22. Which sentence is a summary of the fifth paragraph?

    Ⓐ Some Natural Wonders are different.

    Ⓑ Some Natural Wonders are volcanoes.

    Ⓒ Not all of the Natural Wonders are waterfalls.

    Ⓓ The Natural Wonders are all over the world.

23. What could you predict about being around any of the waterfalls in the article?

    Ⓐ It would be loud.

    Ⓑ It would be dry.

    Ⓒ You would be in Australia.

    Ⓓ You would be more than five miles high.

24. Which question is <u>NOT</u> answered in the article?

    Ⓐ How was the Grand Canyon made?

    Ⓑ Where can the Natural Wonders of the World be found?

    Ⓒ What is a volcano?

    Ⓓ Who picked the places called the Natural Wonders?

Write your answer on the lines below.

25. Why are the things described in this article called "The Natural Wonders of the World"?

_____

_____

Food for Thought

Amy opened the newspaper to the Kid's Corner. "Recipe Contest for Kids!" was printed across the top. Amy was interested. She read on. "The Kid's Corner Crew is looking for new and exciting foods made by and for kids."

Amy decided to enter the contest. What new food would kids like? Amy thought of two things she and her friends always ate, peanut butter sandwiches and macaroni and cheese. What if she put these two foods together? She remembered the spicy peanut sauce that her mother made with noodles. That was one of her favorite dinners. Peanut butter and macaroni wasn't so weird. She tried to think of something else to add. How about strawberry jelly?

That night, when her brother Artie was done cleaning up the kitchen after dinner, Amy got to work. Her mother came in as she was filling a large pot with water. "What are you doing?" her mother cried. "We just ate!" Amy told her mother about the contest. "That's a great idea," her mother said, "but I need to help you with the stove."

Amy and her mother cooked the macaroni and put it in a bowl. Amy added some chunky peanut butter. The peanut butter melted a bit. Peanut pieces stuck to the macaroni. Finally Amy mixed in jelly. Then she got a fork and dug in. "Not bad," Amy said. "But I think it would be better cool, like the way you make the noodles with peanut sauce—or like peanut butter sandwiches." Amy put the bowl in the refrigerator.

The next day Amy wrote down the directions for her new dish. She called it PB&J Pasta. She mailed the recipe to the newspaper. A month later, the winners of the contest were announced in the newspaper. Amy didn't win. She was a little disappointed. She told her father, "I guess the world isn't ready for my wild cooking." Her father picked up the paper. He smiled and pointed to a section called "Almost Winners." Amy turned her eyes to the page. It said:

The judges hated that we could not give prizes for all of the new foods that the city's kids dreamed up. A few recipes should get a special note here. One of the most interesting dishes was sent in by Amy Zhang. Her PB&J Pasta might not make its way into lunch boxes and school cafeterias, but we sure think Amy has great ideas!

GO ON

26. From the information given in the story, which question can you answer?

   Ⓐ How did Amy think up her recipe?

   Ⓑ Who won the recipe contest?

   Ⓒ Why did it take a month for winners to be picked?

   Ⓓ Where does Amy's family live?

27. Why did Amy's mother say she had to help her with the stove?

   Ⓐ She didn't want Amy to break the stove.

   Ⓑ She wanted to make sure Amy won the contest.

   Ⓒ She didn't want Amy to get burned.

   Ⓓ She didn't think Amy had enough good ideas.

28. What do you think would happen if the story went on?

   Ⓐ Amy's mother would not let her cook anymore.

   Ⓑ Amy would keep trying to make new things.

   Ⓒ The people who gave the prizes would tell Amy not to enter again.

   Ⓓ Amy would eat PB&J Pasta every night for dinner.

29. What is the main idea of the story?

   Ⓐ Amy didn't win the contest, but the judges liked her idea.

   Ⓑ Amy's PB&J Pasta will be made for school lunches.

   Ⓒ Amy entered a cooking contest because she knew she would win.

   Ⓓ Amy's parents help her with everything she does.

Write your answer on the lines below.

30. What can you tell about Amy? Include a detail from the story to support what you say about Amy.

_____

_____

George Washington Carver

What if you were not allowed to go to school? What if you had to learn everything you wanted to know about science, art, and music by teaching yourself? That was what life was like for George Washington Carver when he was a boy. He became one of the world's most important scientists and inventors.

George Washington Carver was the son of a slave woman owned by Moses Carver. The Civil War made George free when he was still a child. But Moses Carver's slaves had been moved around so much that by the end of the Civil War, young George was sick. He and his mother were separated. She was never heard from again. George Washington Carver was returned to the farm in Missouri where he was born. He got well and learned how to read and write. As a child, George studied and painted flowers and plants. He also took care of plants. When George was about 10, he set out to get an education.

Many schools did not let in African Americans. Yet in 1890, George Washington Carver became the first black student at Simpson College in Iowa. He studied piano and art, but his teachers thought he was best at growing plants. The next year he became the first African American to study at Iowa State College of Agriculture and Mechanic Arts. Today the school is called Iowa State University. When George was finished studying there, he was asked to stay so he could teach others about growing plants. This made him Iowa State's first African American teacher. He later became a teacher at Alabama's Tuskegee Institute. George Washington Carver did other things, too. He wrote about the studies he did on plants. People also learned from him by reading about his work.

During his life, George Washington Carver made 325 new things out of peanuts. He invented hundreds of ways to use sweet potatoes and other plants that grow in the South. He improved soil used for growing. Most importantly, George Washington Carver made life better for people.

31. Which sentence summarizes this passage?

Ⓐ George Washington Carver studied piano and art, but his teachers thought he was best at planting.

Ⓑ George Washington Carver made life better for many people.

Ⓒ George Washington Carver also wrote about the studies he did on plants.

Ⓓ George Washington Carver became the first African American teacher at Iowa State University.

32. From the passage you can infer that—

Ⓐ George Washington Carver was hard-working.

Ⓑ Many African Americans went to school at the time of the Civil War.

Ⓒ Life was easy for George Washington Carver.

Ⓓ George Washington Carver never wanted to teach at Tuskegee Institute.

33. The main idea of the second paragraph is—

Ⓐ George Washington Carver went to college at age 10.

Ⓑ George Washington Carver became an important inventor.

Ⓒ George Washington Carver was sick.

Ⓓ George Washington Carver had a difficult childhood.

34. Which best tells what this passage is like?

Ⓐ It is historical fiction.   Ⓒ It is a biography.

Ⓑ It is a myth.   Ⓓ It is fiction.

Write your answer on the lines below.

35. Why was it difficult for George Washington Carver to go to school?

_____

_____

STOP

Practice Test 2

Student's Name _____ Grade _____

School Name _____

Teacher's Name _____

Test	Items	Possible Score	Student Score
Vocabulary in Context	1–15	15	
Reading Comprehension	16–35	20	
Total	35	35	

I. Vocabulary
Fill in the letter of the word that best fits in the sentence.

1. The crew worked hard to _____ the man who was trapped under the ice.

   (A) rescue   (C) problem

   (B) jungle   (D) invent

2. Jenna put three slices of _____ on her sandwich.

   (A) chatter   (C) thick

   (B) feast   (D) tomato

3. Many people who have come to America to start a new life have had to _____ to get by.

   (A) drawer   (C) rule

   (B) ruin   (D) struggle

4. His homework was in his bag last night, but what happened to it since is _____.

   (A) a mystery   (C) able

   (B) a choice   (D) an answer

5. James wrote ideas for his next story in his _____.

   (A) life   (C) notebook

   (B) camera   (D) upset

6. Kuan-yin read books about space because she wanted to be a _____ astronaut.

   (A) famous   (C) worse

   (B) past   (D) lazy

7. His family was very _____ when he told them he won first prize.

    Ⓐ leftover   Ⓒ easier

    Ⓑ proud   Ⓓ disturbed

8. With supplies and a map, they set out to _____ the island.

    Ⓐ dinner   Ⓒ explore

    Ⓑ faraway   Ⓓ balance

9. Many times the _____ in folktales are animals.

    Ⓐ characters   Ⓒ myths

    Ⓑ grocery   Ⓓ museum

10. Could you do me a _____ and help me move this box to the attic?

    Ⓐ handle   Ⓒ favor

    Ⓑ package   Ⓓ thankful

11. The flowers on this plant _____ from one to three inches wide.

    Ⓐ range   Ⓒ along

    Ⓑ waxy   Ⓓ wonder

12. The people without umbrellas were _____ during the heavy rain.

    Ⓐ glider   Ⓒ melting

    Ⓑ comfortable   Ⓓ miserable

13. The tourists stopped at an inn during their _____.

Ⓐ conductor   Ⓒ journey

Ⓑ beginning   Ⓓ distance

14. The Patriots decided to _____ an army against Britain.

Ⓐ trade   Ⓒ vote

Ⓑ buzz   Ⓓ form

15. Scientists _____ the bones that were frozen in ice.

Ⓐ decorated   Ⓒ examined

Ⓑ caused   Ⓓ knelt

II. Reading Comprehension
Read each passage. Answer the questions that follow.

It Is Grand

Jared looked across the front seat at his father. His father was humming. "Just a few more miles, Jared," Dad said, "and we will see one of the wonders of the world!"

Driving across the country to see the Grand Canyon was not how Jared wanted to spend the summer. Right now his friends were probably diving into the new city pool. Jared had been looking forward to the new pool all year. He thought back to April, when his dad first told him about the plans he had made for the two of them to drive from Boston to Arizona. He remembered how he started to complain. Then his father began telling him about how he had been saving money and time off from work for this trip. Jared told his friends to have fun without him.

Jared and his father had been driving for over a week. They had been to an amusement park in Pennsylvania. They had visited his aunt in St. Louis. They had slept in a tent in Oklahoma. But most of the time they spent in the car, driving miles and miles west each day.

"Son, this is what we have been waiting for," Jared's dad said suddenly. Jared stared ahead at the huge hole in the earth. He didn't know that the color brown came in so many shades or that it could be so beautiful. The sky was a perfect blue. It was full of puffy clouds that made shadows on the cliffs below. Jared felt so small. But for the first time in his life, he didn't mind feeling small. The world really was wonderful. "Dad," Jared began when he caught his breath, "it was worth every second it took to get here."

GO ON

16. This passage is mostly about—

    Ⓐ things to do in the Grand Canyon.

    Ⓑ the land and rivers in the west.

    Ⓒ a father and son's trip.

    Ⓓ ways to travel across country.

17. How did Jared's dad feel about the trip?

    Ⓐ excited   Ⓒ sad

    Ⓑ bored   Ⓓ nervous

18. What will Jared probably tell his friends when he gets home?

    Ⓐ I wish I had been in the pool instead.

    Ⓑ My father didn't even want to go.

    Ⓒ It doesn't take that long to go from Boston to Arizona.

    Ⓓ The Grand Canyon is beautiful.

19. Which best tells what kind of text this passage is?

    Ⓐ It is a story that could be real.

    Ⓑ It is a fantasy that could not really happen.

    Ⓒ It is a mystery.

    Ⓓ It is a nonfiction science article.

Write your answer on the lines below.

20. What changed Jared's mind about the trip?

_____

_____

The Natural Wonders of the World

You might have heard about the Seven Wonders of the World. They were built by people long ago, although people today aren't sure how. There are also Wonders of the natural world. These are places on Earth that were made by nature, not people.

The Natural Wonders of the World are spread around the earth. There are two in Africa, three in Asia, one in Australia, four in North America, and two in South America.

Four of the Natural Wonders of the World are waterfalls. They are Angel Falls in Venezuela, Iguassu Falls in Brazil and Argentina, Niagara Falls in Canada and the United States, and Victoria Falls in Zambia and Zimbabwe. Angel Falls is the largest waterfall in the world. It is 3,212 feet high and 500 feet wide. At these waterfalls, a great amount of water flows quickly over high rocks and crashes far below.

Three of the Natural Wonders are mountains. They are Mount Everest in Nepal, Mount Fuji in Japan, and Mount Kilimanjaro in Tanzania. Mount Everest is the highest point on Earth. It is 29,028 feet tall. That is almost five miles high or almost as tall as 20 Empire State Buildings stacked on top of each other!

Two of the Natural Wonders of the World are volcanoes. A volcano is a hole in the earth that sometimes lets out hot rock and ash. Often a mountain or hill forms around the hole when the rock and ash cool. Krakatoa Island in Indonesia and Paracutin Volcano in Mexico are both Natural Wonders.

The other Natural Wonders of the World are much different. The Bay of Fundy in Canada has the highest and strongest tides in the world. It is home to more whales than anywhere else. The Great Barrier Reef off the coast of Australia is another Natural Wonder that is home to many animals. The Great Barrier Reef is made of the skeletons of tiny sea creatures that have built up over millions of years. It is more than 1,250 miles long. The last Natural Wonder of the World is the Grand Canyon in the United States. The Grand Canyon is a long, narrow valley in Arizona that was formed by water cutting through the ground. Many people travel to the Grand Canyon every year to see interesting shapes of rocks and beautiful colors.

GO ON ▶

21. Which is the <u>most important</u> idea of the article?

   Ⓐ Mount Everest is 29,028 feet tall.

   Ⓑ There are four Natural Wonders in North America.

   Ⓒ The Natural Wonders were made by nature.

   Ⓓ Many people travel to the Grand Canyon every year.

22. Which sentence is a summary of the fifth paragraph?

   Ⓐ Some Natural Wonders are different.

   Ⓑ Some Natural Wonders are volcanoes.

   Ⓒ Not all of the Natural Wonders are waterfalls.

   Ⓓ The Natural Wonders are all over the world.

23. What could you predict about being around any of the waterfalls in the article?

   Ⓐ It would be loud.

   Ⓑ It would be dry.

   Ⓒ You would be in Australia.

   Ⓓ You would be more than five miles high.

24. Which question is <u>NOT</u> answered in the article?

   Ⓐ How was the Grand Canyon made?

   Ⓑ Where can the Natural Wonders of the World be found?

   Ⓒ What is a volcano?

   Ⓓ Who picked the places called the Natural Wonders?

Write your answer on the lines below.

25. Why are the things described in this article called "The Natural Wonders of the World"?

   _____

   _____

Food for Thought

Amy opened the newspaper to the Kid's Corner. "Recipe Contest for Kids!" was printed across the top. Amy was interested. She read on. "The Kid's Corner Crew is looking for new and exciting foods made by and for kids."

Amy decided to enter the contest. What new food would kids like? Amy thought of two things she and her friends always ate, peanut butter sandwiches and macaroni and cheese. What if she put these two foods together? She remembered the spicy peanut sauce that her mother made with noodles. That was one of her favorite dinners. Peanut butter and macaroni wasn't so weird. She tried to think of something else to add. How about strawberry jelly?

That night, when her brother Artie was done cleaning up the kitchen after dinner, Amy got to work. Her mother came in as she was filling a large pot with water. "What are you doing?" her mother cried. "We just ate!" Amy told her mother about the contest. "That's a great idea," her mother said, "but I need to help you with the stove."

Amy and her mother cooked the macaroni and put it in a bowl. Amy added some chunky peanut butter. The peanut butter melted a bit. Peanut pieces stuck to the macaroni. Finally Amy mixed in jelly. Then she got a fork and dug in. "Not bad," Amy said. "But I think it would be better cool, like the way you make the noodles with peanut sauce—or like peanut butter sandwiches." Amy put the bowl in the refrigerator.

The next day Amy wrote down the directions for her new dish. She called it PB&J Pasta. She mailed the recipe to the newspaper. A month later, the winners of the contest were announced in the newspaper. Amy didn't win. She was a little disappointed. She told her father, "I guess the world isn't ready for my wild cooking." Her father picked up the paper. He smiled and pointed to a section called "Almost Winners." Amy turned her eyes to the page. It said:

> The judges hated that we could not give prizes for all of the new foods that the city's kids dreamed up. A few recipes should get a special note here. One of the most interesting dishes was sent in by Amy Zhang. Her PB&J Pasta might not make its way into lunch boxes and school cafeterias, but we sure think Amy has great ideas!

GO ON

26. From the information given in the story, which question can you answer?

Ⓐ How did Amy think up her recipe?

Ⓑ Who won the recipe contest?

Ⓒ Why did it take a month for winners to be picked?

Ⓓ Where does Amy's family live?

27. Why did Amy's mother say she had to help her with the stove?

Ⓐ She didn't want Amy to break the stove.

Ⓑ She wanted to make sure Amy won the contest.

Ⓒ She didn't want Amy to get burned.

Ⓓ She didn't think Amy had enough good ideas.

28. What do you think would happen if the story went on?

Ⓐ Amy's mother would not let her cook anymore.

Ⓑ Amy would keep trying to make new things.

Ⓒ The people who gave the prizes would tell Amy not to enter again.

Ⓓ Amy would eat PB&J Pasta every night for dinner.

29. What is the main idea of the story?

Ⓐ Amy didn't win the contest, but the judges liked her idea.

Ⓑ Amy's PB&J Pasta will be made for school lunches.

Ⓒ Amy entered a cooking contest because she knew she would win.

Ⓓ Amy's parents help her with everything she does.

Write your answer on the lines below.

30. What can you tell about Amy? Include a detail from the story to support what you say about Amy.

_____

_____

T22 Practice Test 2

George Washington Carver

What if you were not allowed to go to school? What if you had to learn everything you wanted to know about science, art, and music by teaching yourself? That was what life was like for George Washington Carver when he was a boy. He became one of the world's most important scientists and inventors.

George Washington Carver was the son of a slave woman owned by Moses Carver. The Civil War made George free when he was still a child. But Moses Carver's slaves had been moved around so much that by the end of the Civil War, young George was sick. He and his mother were separated. She was never heard from again. George Washington Carver was returned to the farm in Missouri where he was born. He got well and learned how to read and write. As a child, George studied and painted flowers and plants. He also took care of plants. When George was about 10, he set out to get an education.

Many schools did not let in African Americans. Yet in 1890, George Washington Carver became the first black student at Simpson College in Iowa. He studied piano and art, but his teachers thought he was best at growing plants. The next year he became the first African American to study at Iowa State College of Agriculture and Mechanic Arts. Today the school is called Iowa State University. When George was finished studying there, he was asked to stay so he could teach others about growing plants. This made him Iowa State's first African American teacher. He later became a teacher at Alabama's Tuskegee Institute. George Washington Carver did other things, too. He wrote about the studies he did on plants. People also learned from him by reading about his work.

During his life, George Washington Carver made 325 new things out of peanuts. He invented hundreds of ways to use sweet potatoes and other plants that grow in the South. He improved soil used for growing. Most importantly, George Washington Carver made life better for people.

GO ON ▶

31. Which sentence summarizes this passage?

   Ⓐ George Washington Carver studied piano and art, but his teachers thought he was best at planting.

   Ⓑ George Washington Carver made life better for many people.

   Ⓒ George Washington Carver also wrote about the studies he did on plants.

   Ⓓ George Washington Carver became the first African American teacher at Iowa State University.

32. From the passage you can infer that—

   Ⓐ George Washington Carver was hard-working.

   Ⓑ Many African Americans went to school at the time of the Civil War.

   Ⓒ Life was easy for George Washington Carver.

   Ⓓ George Washington Carver never wanted to teach at Tuskegee Institute.

33. The main idea of the second paragraph is—

   Ⓐ George Washington Carver went to college at age 10.

   Ⓑ George Washington Carver became an important inventor.

   Ⓒ George Washington Carver was sick.

   Ⓓ George Washington Carver had a difficult childhood.

34. Which best tells what this passage is like?

   Ⓐ It is historical fiction.   Ⓒ It is a biography.

   Ⓑ It is a myth.   Ⓓ It is fiction.

Write your answer on the lines below.

35. Why was it difficult for George Washington Carver to go to school?

_____

_____